The Gates of Light

by

Pari Forood

West Cornwall Publishing

West Cornwall Publishing Company

340 River Road
West Cornwall, CT 06796

Cover design by Riverdog Grafix

Printed in the United States
Shipped to our readers by the United States Postal Service

ISBN 978-0-9884503-2-5

❖

This book is dedicated to every first generation American who is here now and those to come.

❖

❖

Author's Note

In crafting this story of my life and my family's history, I delved deep into my past and my ancestry to uncover both misperceptions and truths. I wanted to demystify the Persian people, Iran, Islam and a congressional office. I also wanted to join the conversation about our country's need for immigration reform. In this process, I took liberties in writing portions of the book, particularly concerning my cousin's flight from Iran. I did not have the opportunity to meet some of the people he came in contact with or who were involved in that process, therefore, many of these characters are fictitious or I have given them fictitious thoughts and feelings. The rest of the story is entirely from my memory and results either from my many conversations with the principals or my personal experience. Any errors are mine and mine alone. In order to absolve any culpability or involvement, I have disguised some people and changed their names.

❖

"One of my biggest regrets is that we were not able to get comprehensive immigration reform. America has always been able to attract the most ambitious people who are determined to have a better life. If we ever lose that and start to believe that somehow that it is instead a threat to us to have those people come here, we are going to lose one of the strongest elements of not just our national wealth, but our national soul. Sometimes I wanted to say, 'Check your last name. It doesn't sound like it came over on the Mayflower.'"

-Condoleeza Rice, 2009

❖

My parents' wedding, Congregational Church, Hancock, ME

Introduction

I come from tea. This is the first line of a poem written by my daughter when she was in the sixth grade. I know why she wrote it. Each and every morning and each and every afternoon, my father drinks tea: Assam in the morning, Darjeeling in the afternoon and most often with dried fruit — figs, apricots, raisins, dates — whatever is available. When Persians get together, they drink tea, always in a glass. My two daughters drink tea, I drink tea, my sisters drink tea. I had a brief flirtation with coffee in college and when in Italy I can't wait to have a cappuccino but we are tea people probably because we come from tea.

When you make tea, you place loose tea leaves into a receptacle and pour boiling water over them. The leaves rise to the top as individual elements, separate and apart until, after three or four minutes they settle to the depths, heaped and saturated, and you are rewarded for your patience with a drink that is at once calming and reviving, neutral enough to want anytime and yet distinctive enough to eclipse all comparison with water; initially separate and apart only to join together to become one, in a complete and satisfying ending.

And that is what we are — a nation, separate and apart, individuals streaming forth from different fonts only to land on common ground and congeal and unify. That is the experiment we are all a part of with the end result still unknown.

I, too, am a part of this experiment with my interesting background and reflective nature, and I was pulled into a forced reconciliation with my past rather suddenly with a phone call.

In a stunning statement declared by my daughter as she was putting together the course schedule for her last semester of college, she told me that she wanted to study Farsi. I couldn't imagine why as the only places she could speak it would be Iran, Afghanistan, Turkmenistan and Los Angeles, California, but she persisted despite my misgivings (as usual), and said that she wanted to take it because she is part Persian.

"Well, I am an even bigger part Persian and I have no desire to speak Farsi," I told her.

"And I have never understood that!" she said. "How can you have a name like Pari Forood and not want to speak the language of the place where that name comes from?"

I could feel her smile. Every part of what makes her different and unique is welcome to her. In fact, she looks more Persian than I do. For some reason the genes for dark hair and eyes and eyelashes jumped right over me, ignored her father, and landed on her face.

She continued. "I think it would make Pop Pop proud. I want to see his expression when I speak Farsi to him."

Yes, I would like to see that too. I knew it would conjure up some emotions that my father had buried for so long. I don't remember him ever being proud of his homeland, he was too busy being proud of America and his American family. And yet, when he took my sisters and me to Iran when we were young, he showed us Tehran and the countryside all the way to the Caspian Sea, with pleasure and a certain sense of pride. We met relatives we didn't know we had and since only a few spoke English, we just smiled and hugged and tried to blend in at the endless parties they gave in our honor.

"It was the Hostage Crisis in 1979 that served as the final straw for him," I told her.

Once the Shah was overthrown and unyielding theocracy was established, I think his disappointment turned to disgust and he realized he would never be able to go back and visit his parents or his brother and sister. He focused on bringing his nephews to the U.S. and severed all emotional ties with Iran.

"You can't deny your ancestry," she reminded me. "Being Persian is about so much more than being born in Iran. It ties you to an ancient culture and religion not to mention one of the great empires in history!"

True, there was a good deal to be proud of or at the very least interested in learning about. I was familiar with this itch of hers; I had it when I was in college. I took an ancient civilization course in the hopes of learning more about the Persian Empire and its kings and culture but the class was all about Greece and Rome with only a cursory nod to the Greeks' ancient enemy to the north. By the time I graduated in 1980 and arrived in Washington, D.C., I was bright-eyed and ready to shape policy and effect change. The first time someone asked me about my name I lied and said it was Egyptian like King Farouk.

"Iran is in the Gang of Three or Unholy Alliance or whatever 'Bush 43' called it," I reminded her. "Why would you want to learn the language of the sworn enemy of your country?"

"I think you are trying to come up with 'Axis of Evil'" she chided me, "and besides, our problems are with the current regime. Who's to say the brave men and women of Iran won't rise up and overthrow the mullahs and establish democracy? Our problem is not with the Persian people, like our relatives, it is with the autocratic government and their treatment of its citizens."

That was certainly accurate. I once saw a documentary hosted by CNN's Christiane Amanpour, whose father is Persian, where she went around Iran and interviewed people in the street, on their farm, at various businesses and none of them had a problem with the U.S. One woman said she didn't want her daughters watching American

4

television because she was afraid they would grow up to be "like Brittany Spears." Well, I didn't want my daughters growing up to be like Brittany Spears either!

This conversation was becoming interesting and I welcomed the opportunity to talk more, explore my feelings and hers. I couldn't help but feel a certain sense of irony that my daughter, named after my very WASPy maternal grandmother, was the most interested in her Persian heritage.

She continued to make her case. "I was the only one who didn't fall asleep when you were reading *A Thousand and One Nights* and I remember you teasing us that you almost named one of us Scheherazade! And that poem, something about a 'Peri' flying around looking for a way into heaven? All of that and playing backgammon instead of monopoly, Pop Pop's rice and *Khoresht-e Badem-jan* casserole, and afternoon tea in a glass, not a cup, with figs or dates make us part Persian and different, Mom, whether we look like it or not."

This is also true. Harvard sociologist, Horace Kallen, wrote "fulfillment in life is a function of cultural identity, that cultural identity is a function of ethnicity and that ethnicity is immutable." He went on to say that "racial ancestry is the one unalterable constituent of self-hood, and the happiness people pursue in their lives has its form implied in ancestral endowment." (Kallen, 1915) Know yourself and your provenance and forever be whole.

And that is why this story must be told, for everyone who missed the Mayflower or wondered if they were burdened or graced by their heritage. This is the story of a journey from ignorance to enlightenment, from disillusion to inspiration, and from restlessness to peace.

Part I

The glorious Angel who was keeping

The Gates of Light beheld her weeping,

And as he nearer drew and listened

To her sad song, a tear-drop glistened

Within his eyelids, like the spray

From Eden's fountain when it lies

On the blue flower which, Bramins say,

Blooms nowhere but in Paradise.

"Nymph of a fair but erring line!"

Gently he said, "One hope is thine.

'Tis written in the Book of Fate,

The Peri yet may be forgiven

Who brings to this Eternal gate

The Gift that is most dear to Heaven!

Go seek it and redeem thy sin —

'Tis sweet to let the Pardoned in."

Paradise and the Peri from *Lalla Rookh* (1817)
by Sir Thomas Moore (1779-1852)

6

❖

Tehran, Iran, May, 1984

He awoke in the only bedroom he had ever known in the house that belonged to his family. As his eyes rested on each object with resignation and sadness, he felt the weight of his circumstances paralyze his body like a crippling disease. It was 4:00 a.m. and he knew his mother would come to wake him, make his last breakfast and say goodbye, maybe forever.

She knocked. "Are you awake? Hurry and get dressed, your father is ready," she spoke with urgency. She was trying to hide her fear and despondency at the thought of losing her son.

"Yes, I will be there in a minute."

He always attempted to please her; this was the duty of a son to his mother, in any culture, and he would not keep her waiting this last time. In truth, he was the easiest of her three sons — congenial, calm, and even-tempered — unlike his volatile brothers. As the middle child, he was the peacemaker between the older and the youngest. It was ironic that the mandatory conscription for the war between Iran and Iraq escalated to coincide with his 17th birthday, drafting the least appropriate soldier and martyr.

After the letter arrived demanding that Sahand report for training and induction in three weeks, his family made the difficult decision to pay for his escape to Pakistan. In Karachi, he could purchase a passport in the notorious black market, fly to France where his uncle worked, and then to America to attend college with a student visa. His older brother was already in California in graduate school and he would join him there, *Inshallah*, God willing.

The Foroods were never religious people. Strongly influenced by the western culture ushered in by the British and French after World War I, as well as by two pro-Western Persian kings, they emulated the customs of French imperialism. Sahand's father spent his early childhood in Paris where his father was attending military college. The family boasted a fluency in French and knowledge of Western music, fashion and food all favored by the bourgeoisie of Tehran. His uncle had gone to America as a student, married an American, worked for an American company, and raised three American daughters: the last time he came to Iran was sixteen years ago to introduce his daughters to his family. Relatives lived in Switzerland, France, Germany and the U.S. A war over border disputes that had been waging off and on for centuries was so inconsequential to this family that the thought of sending a member to be killed by Iraqi chemical weapons was unthinkable.

His mother put the tea in a glass in front of him as he sat down.

"They drink tea in a cup in America, your brother tells us." She tried to sound cheerful. "You will be having breakfast in your uncle's home in California in a few days."

The hope in her voice embodied the universal mother's prayer of protection and security. She refused to allow the diffidence in her heart to creep into her throat or demeanor. She would serve his food just as she had every morning for seventeen years, knowing tomorrow he would be out of her cocoon of maternal comforting.

I am losing my second son, she thought. Her helplessness sucked her energy like the tide carrying waves out to sea.

His father walked into the kitchen. "It is time to go," he announced.

His son resembled him in stature. They were both fair for Persians and had no facial hair, giving them a look of continental universality and therefore, acceptance. However, the one trait that set them apart from others was their height. Sahand stood at six feet, six inches, and his father, who was only slightly smaller, took after the Turkish ancestors said to be part of the family generations ago when the Ottoman and Persian Empires were also warring neighbors.

He is tall and strong like the mountain he is named for, his mother thought, *he will not get hurt, they will not rob him in Pakistan, he will not be stabbed while dealing with the thieves who sell the false passports.*

As she hugged her son, she realized that she would gladly, freely, give her life for him; if she could march into an Iraqi assault, she would. But interfering with the intricate plan of getting him out of Iran would cause his discovery and imprisonment, so she was forced to resign herself to the confluence of fate and luck.

They left in the diesel Mercedes his father purchased with great pride five years before the Islamic Revolution forced the denunciation of any demonstrations of Western preference. Rials were sewn into Sahand's clothes, under the soles of his shoes, in a belt around his waist, with which to bribe truck drivers, border guards and pay for a passport and plane ticket to freedom.

He tried to feel excited and adventurous, to instill some positive element into this moment and unburden his father. He thought of America and his favorite song, "Eye of the Tiger." He thought of his brother's phone calls from California describing the girls' short skirts, watching *Charlie's Angels* on television, and the supermarkets' overabundance of junk food.

As they approached the appointed meeting place on the outskirts of barren and rocky Tehran, there was no truck in sight and Sahand felt relief from his dreaded task. His father parked and got out of the car, nervously fingering the large wad of cash in his pocket. They waited an hour for the vehicle with a *Pepsi* logo on the side to arrive, unable to speak to each other but silently communicating their mutual support. And as the sky lightened to embrace the coming day, both men felt the irrepressible hope that comes with a new dawn. They knew they would have to trust people along this journey that could take days, weeks or months and end in disaster or discovery.

His father handed the driver his cash and turned to look into the eyes of his son. Neither could speak as they embraced and both felt a cold grip on their throat muscles.

A part of me is being ripped away, his father thought, *a piece of my being that was never intended to leave my sphere of influence is now torn from my body.*

He watched the truck pull away with his son in the back amidst bottles of orange *Fanta* and *Canada Dry* ginger ale. As the sun broke free from the low horizon, a glow arose from the earth to illuminate the road for this wayward traveler who would be forced to age and grow with this crossing. In the coming weeks he would be introduced to all elements of humanity, both base and brave, and forced to ride on the capricious wave of fortune.

His father stood in the desolation of a field on the fringes of Tehran. Memories of the quiet little boy who loved to look at the night sky and throw pistachio shells from the roof garden and fall asleep in his arms came flooding to him. As a father, he wished he could see into the future and feel reassured of peace for his children and grandchildren, but all he felt was the stark realization that they were all in fate's hands.

My business card, 1983

Capitol Hill, Washington, D.C. May, 1984

"Which part of this is true?" he asked.

"What do you mean which part, it's all true." I countered.

"Since when did changes in copyright laws become 'the most important issue facing the Judiciary Committee in the 98th Congress'?" The Administrative Assistant and my immediate boss had sarcasm dripping from his smoke-stained vocal chords.

I had been working as Press Secretary to Congressman Hamilton Fish, Jr., moderate Republican of New York for two years, and the most exciting thing I had written about was obscure legislation to instigate tort reform. I tried to imagine myself as Teddy Roosevelt's aide, talking to the press about breaking up Standard Oil but no matter how colorful or hyperbolic my phrasing, aside from the American Bar Journal, I couldn't get one periodical to print anything.

Once, when the *Today Show* called to ask if we had a comment on a recent Supreme Court ruling, I thought I would faint with glee. We taped a response in the television studio of the Rayburn House Office Building across the street from the Capitol, only to watch with dashed hope the next morning as the story was eclipsed by a mudslide in southern California.

"Don't sweat it. Our man has a great reputation in the home district. He gets elected by seventy-two percent every two years and the local press love him." The Administrative Assistant, John Barry, number two in the office after the Congressman, was attempting to assuage my bruised ego. In truth, all he cared about was reelection, his job, his pension and his sailboat on the Chesapeake, in that order.

Encouraging words were rare coming from Barry, who kept the quote from *Dante's Inferno* on a hand-painted sign in large letters above his door: *Abandon Hope All Ye Who Enter Here*. At Monday morning staff meetings, he would look at us with disdain and say, "Youth is wasted on the young." It was tough to be upbeat around him but he was a backboard when you needed it. He reminded me of a character from a Studs Terkel novel — Irish, crusty, foul-mouthed, "proud member of Uncle Sam's Naval Forces from WW Dos" with nicotine stained fingers and voice.

Barry refused to use the intercom and just shouted for us by last name. "Forood!" he would bellow from his desk,

"Persian Princess! I need to see that newsletter you are writing to make sure you haven't given anyone else credit for any of our initiatives like you usually do!" This was his idea of softening the blow before he would cross out seventy-five percent of the copy I had painstakingly written.

The fact that I was half-Persian intrigued him. "People used to be Irish, Italian, German or Jewish. Now we have God-damned Persians in this country!" Then he would smile and make me feel both lucky and cursed that I was working for him.

Barry was impressed that I was a political science major from Vassar, a college he begrudgingly admired, though his memory was tainted by images of debutantes in saddle shoes running to grab the train to husband-hunt at Yale. His education was definitely more the 'school of life' type. I would sometimes see him physically tense with resentment toward lobbyists wearing Armani suits and reeking of entitlement.

None of us would have admitted that we jockeyed for his approval. We were all better educated, had more social graces and cultural experience, yet we admired him for making the right political call every time. Barry knew his business and he had achieved a degree of success without any of our inherited license. When he met Hamilton Fish, Jr., or HF, as we called him — uber-privileged son and grandson of Senators and Congressmen, progeny of Revolutionary War heroes, Reconstructionist Innovators, and WWII isolationists — it was a congenial match only advanced physics could explain.

HF was Ivy League educated and had that air of insouciance only those with direct ties to the Founding Fathers or one of "Mrs. Astor's Four Hundred" could

14

possibly possess. He wore old Brooks Brothers suits every day, left over from his Milbank, Tweed, Hadley & McCloy days and probably gardened in them at his house in Millbrook. His air of formality was punctuated by a wink or a deep-throated laugh when he admired a statement or thought. Even though he had one hundred times more money than any of us, he never had cash and was always asking one of us to get him a sandwich or cup of soup. Of course, we would all dive for the phone when we saw him coming and act like we were terribly engaged in conversation so as to avoid paying for his meal.

When the bells rang for a vote on the House floor, he used to emerge from his office and beckon one of us to follow him through marbled halls, each the length of football fields, to the elevators and underground train to the Capitol. There, we would catch him up on the subject of the vote or the timbre of the mail or in my case ideas for mass communications with our constituents. He was six feet, four inches tall with a stride one and a half of mine; I had to run to keep up, talk fast, breathe and think all at the same time.

Congressmen have fifteen minutes to get to the House floor for a recorded vote so he always moved quickly and to add to the mayhem, other Members were rushing out of their offices with staff congesting hall traffic like Grand Central Station at 5:00 on a weeknight.

Once when we reached the 'Members Only' elevator, he guided me in to that privileged, packed space, and asked me to write something down.

"I didn't bring a pad." I said softly, trying not to engage the twenty other Members in the conversation. "Or a pencil."

"What!?" he exclaimed "Don't they teach proper dictation technique at Vassar anymore?"

The elevator erupted in good humor and I was trying to figure out how to laugh, be a good sport and poison his coffee all at the same time. And then he was off with a wink and a winning smile and the mad dash to the underground train to the Capitol Building.

In truth, I loved working for him and didn't envy any of the other Press Secretaries even in the Senate or White House. When the Senate was passing historic legislation on Floor Debate, HF urged us to stop whatever we were doing and get over to the Senate Visitor's Gallery to witness it. He told me to read Edmund Burke and the Scottish philosophers and all the history I could because, "What is past is surely prologue." And he urged me to feel special and lucky for my background because it was fascinating and colorful and made me interesting to speak to and to look at.

"We are all immigrants in this country, judged not by our ancestry but by our accomplishments," I wrote in a speech he gave at a naturalization ceremony in White Plains, New York. He called afterward to tell me it was one of the most profound things he had ever uttered in public. I told him I believed it wholeheartedly and I hoped he felt the same. He assured me he did and that for the first time in his life, felt jealous when addressing those fresh pilgrims, unfettered by a family tree laden with the fruits, both damaged and clean, of a weighty past.

Before I started working for him, he was a freshman member of Congress when President Nixon's impeachment came before the House Judiciary Committee. By the laws in the U.S. Constitution, the House Judiciary Committee determines if impeachment is merited and if so, the President is tried before the full House of Representatives. As a minority Republican and lowest ranking member of the committee, he had to cast his vote first. It was expected that the vote go along party lines: Republicans voting against impeachment and majority Democrats voting in favor; thereby, in a foregone conclusion bringing the charges against the President to the House floor.

I heard that Congressman Fish struggled with this decision, spending many hours writing old-fashioned briefs on long yellow legal pads, just as he did in law school at NYU twenty years before. Ultimately, when asked to voice his conviction, he did not succumb to Party pressure and voted with the Democrats in favor of impeachment. This caused a rift between him and his former-Congressman father that never healed. You could see this bare honesty on his face and in his stature. He could never lie to anyone, never be that smarmy politician who made promises he couldn't keep. This is why God gave him John Barry and the symbiosis kept things humming in the 21st Congressional District of New York.

I should have been satisfied with my modest accomplishments and our good working relationship, but I couldn't help but want to take him, my box of Corn Flakes, if you will, national. I toiled daily, thinking of ways to make him more appealing to the public. What I didn't realize at the time was that he had no interest in a higher office. He was a "good egg," as F. Scott Fitzgerald would have considered him, content to do good things for the half a million people he represented. When we received a phone call from a constituent from the "other" party or who organized fundraisers for our opponent, John Barry would put it on the bottom of the call-back list and tell HF not to bother. But the Congressman would always ignore him, reasoning that even if they didn't support *us* or vote for *us*, now that *we* are elected, *we* represent everyone. I think he liked using "we," sharing the blame as well as triumphs with all four hundred thirty-four Members of the House of Representatives, not to mention us, his staff.

No matter the tangible lack of personal successes, I felt lucky. There were at least fifty people who wanted my job. Working on "the Hill," as it is known, is viewed as prestigious; the only reason we toiled ridiculous hours for peanuts. My father took one look at my business card with the imperial eagle surrounded by a gold embossed wreath (logo for the U.S. Congress) and was rendered speechless. He was never impressed by the fact that my salary barely paid my rent, phone bill and electricity, however. If I wasn't invited out to dinner for the last week of the month, I didn't eat.

Despite the low pay and subsequent inability to purchase anything but the necessities, having to rely on parents for vacations, and not having to worry about dieting, the U.S. Congress was the greatest place on Earth and the only place I ever wanted to be. I remember writing a report in the fifth grade on the President and his cabinet and wondering which appointment I would enjoy, given my choice of Secretary of State or Health, Education and Welfare. All of these jobs came with a level of cachet I considered greater than all of the wealth in the world. Power was my aphrodisiac (even though I wouldn't have characterized it in that way at the time), and it just seemed more desirable to be making national policy than money.

And that distinguished me from just about every one of my classmates and my pragmatic father.

My father never understood the allure of power. He was very practical. Coming to this country from Iran as a seventeen-year-old with a limited grasp of English and a strict allowance, he had to hone his skills considerably and even though he received the best private education America had to offer, he was acutely aware of his outsider status.

When he was playing varsity soccer at Hackley prep school in Westchester County, New York, the coach asked him his name.

"Farokh," my dad replied with the guttural sounds common to Farsi, Arabic and Hebrew.

The coach was mystified. "Pick another name, something we can call on the field when we want to pass you the ball."

After a moment my father said, "Robert" remembering the name from a Hollywood movie he had seen in Iran and like magic, his American persona was born.

While my father was busy learning English at prep school then earning undergraduate and graduate degrees in chemical engineering at Columbia University in New York City, my mother was majoring in sculpture at Bennington College in Vermont. Two more different people did not exist in the world: she with blond hair and blue eyes and the youngest of five, helplessly spoiled by her father; and he with dark hair, olive skin and a penchant for chemistry, math and strong discipline.

Engineers are special people. Their brains work in a methodical, arithmetic way and not just in school or business. My father used to open up the dishwasher and if plates and glasses weren't stacked in perfect order for optimal cleaning, he would rearrange everything. He didn't understand tears, tantrums or trauma. Every situation demanded a calm reaction based on Euclidian geometry. He did his taxes with the help of a slide rule. But I see now that his pragmatism was born of necessity. Far from home, far from the family he could fall back on, he became acutely rational and stoic. Like a young tree forced to grow on unfamiliar soil, he girded his inner strength to face the storm of the unknown. I don't know if he became tougher as he aged or if he was born that way but when my sisters and I heard stories of his childhood pranks we were truly shocked: one tale involved his brother, cousins and him, almost burning down a house by lighting fire crackers inside. I still try to reconcile that mischievous Persian boy with the stern father I know.

After his initial successes in high school soccer, college, business, matrimony and fatherhood, 'Robert' resembled the typical California dad: commuting to work, playing tennis on weekends and barbequing hot dogs and hamburgers for his highly emotional, all-female family. We went to church without him. He always looked mystified at our raucous Christmas morning pandemonium, and yet he was proud of his successful assimilation into the American way of life.

Hearing about his early life, it always struck me as suspiciously conflict-free and happy. I was wary of his memories of post-World War II America and the perfect picture he drew of New York City and its environs — not the reality of dirty streets or disparity of wealth or racial tensions but the promise of possibility so absent in Iran.

The first thing he noticed of Americans was their laughter and light-heartedness. In Iran, they were happy, especially the well-off, but the joviality was tempered by a history colored by tragedy and a complex national personality, as a beautiful Persian rug, so colorful and intricate, woven with the triumphs and sorrows of a three thousand-year-old culture. But now I see that he was ripe for America, free of obligation to his past and rich family history, serving as colorful background to a future he himself created.

❖

A Typical Congressional Office

I rented a house in Georgetown with two friends; one worked for the Environmental Protection Agency, the other toiled endlessly for a philanthropic organization saving the whales. You would think that roommate #1 and roommate #2 were in collusion considering their shared mission to guard the environment, but in truth they agreed on nothing. They deferred to me to settle arguments and I found myself pathetically lacking as a competent moral compass.

In fact, as the neutral party working for the U.S. Congress and charged with the public's trust to help pass the Clean Water Act, Clean Air Act and the Superfund (Environmental Cleanup) Act, I was least interested in the facts and most concerned with the public's perception of them. This is the rule of thumb in politics: if it is popular, get behind it; if it is controversial, consider it; if it is anathema to the majority, condemn it. Who decides this? Congressional staff, of course, and everyone knows that staff run the world.

The Hill is populated with approximately ten thousand House staff, four thousand Senate staff and hundreds of committee staff. Add to that the influx of three thousand interns every summer (some paid and some living on their

22

parents' largesse) and you can see how we outnumbered the elected officials in a comfortable thirty-five to one ratio.

According to the Congressional Management Foundation, Congress is not an attractive place to work: "Staff typically work exceedingly long, unpredictable hours that leave little time for outside activities, receive lower pay than both private sector and federal executive branch staff, work in cramped quarters with no privacy, exercise minimal control over their work schedules, and have virtually no job security," (CMF, 2013).

So why did we want to be there? Why did the Personnel Office keep hundreds of resumes on file from hundreds of recent college graduates dying to perform menial tasks at entry-level positions for which they were exceedingly overqualified? Because someone, somewhere, divulged the secret that staff are really in charge. If we thought we were overworked or burning out, at least we didn't have to fly to Houston or San Diego or Portland every weekend and answer to sometimes irate and sometimes fawning constituents. I wondered how Alaska and Hawaii Congressmen still stood after a weekend of rubber-chicken dinners and Eagle Scout ceremonies at the local high school. They would arrive back in Washington Tuesday morning, exhausted or charged by the revelation of some injustice and we would all struggle with another week of "heavy and growing workloads, long and unpredictable hours, and work demands that too often force staff to sacrifice quality for quantity," (CMF, 2013).

What the CMF does not take into account is the compensatory effect of the heady influence of power. The Member of Congress may ultimately be voting on legislation or questioning witnesses at committee hearings or deciding funding levels in private meetings but on a daily basis, we staff made judgment calls and determinations affecting current and future policy for tens of thousands of people.

Committee staffs, with their advanced degrees and areas of expertise, are the information source for every committee where most of the policy work is done. When a Member is grilling a Cabinet Secretary or Executive Branch Administrator, star baseball pitcher or CEO of an automobile company, questions are researched and written by committee staff. And when the hearing is over, the material gleaned from the witnesses and testifiers is poured over and turned into recommendations by committee staff.

At the personal staff level, we were charged with the management of crises in the district, briefings on the vote both oral and written, and in my case, shaping public perception of everything from votes and initiatives to HF's conduct and demeanor.

"What is it?" HF would shout into the large staff room as he was running to cast his vote on the House floor. Most times we would have to follow him down the hall explaining the vote and the party recommendation or how the mail was running on the subject. The job was overwhelming and the rest of the time we were just suffocating under the crushing weight of a million pieces of paper.

Each Member is allowed twenty-two staff between their Washington and district offices. The Washington office is the most heavily populated, as that is where the greatest concentration of work culminates. However, we had three district offices manned with dedicated local folk who were very familiar with the nuances of the area and proved invaluable to effective representation.

Dolly manned the Peekskill office and with her long red braid and friendly manner she charmed everyone in a fifty-mile radius. There wasn't a man, woman or child reluctant to call her to make the Congressman aware of some impending doom or local celebration or ribbon-cutting ceremony. The Poughkeepsie office had three paid staff and usually a volunteer or two. This is where the bulk of the case work was done: helping people receive veterans' benefits, settling erroneous IRS investigations, resolving Medicaid and Medicare problems and relieving the Washington staff of the onslaught of the four hundred pieces of mail each week.

Our third office in Kingston was manned by 'Johnny Nock' and Tia. I am not sure what they accomplished other than populating this outpost and making sure the people of Ulster County felt happy and included. Johnny Nock (whose last name was shortened for expediency) was the Congressman's official driver. Nock developed such a rapport with HF for twenty years that his grandson was christened, Hamilton Fish Noccarato.

This group of colorful, native mid-state New Yorkers kept us informed and connected to our constituency — essential elements of any successful Congressional office. The last thing you want to hear is that a Congressman has 'gone Washington' or become oblivious to his roots. We sent HF back to the district as often as we could and his face showed the strain like old shoe leather after years of pounding the pavement.

One of the perks of working for a Congressman with seniority was the invitations to receptions. HF would accept the important ones and sometimes we would accompany him but most often, ten or twelve engraved announcements of the arrival in Washington of the Shellfish Society of America or the Local Chapters of the National Chamber of Commerce would prompt the disbursement of office talent to the cocktail circuit in the Gulag Archipelago of Congressional and Federal Office Buildings.

Since it was a Thursday, prime party night, I was armed with two invitations to the NW part of town. I put the top down on my Triumph Spitfire, made a silent prayer to the gods of British motorcars for it to start, and drove to the Sheraton to meet any business people who may have come down from Hudson Valley. It was an essential part of the art of complicity and commutation to convince them that I was, in fact, very important and not to be disappointed that the Congressman had better receptions to attend and more important people to meet. I secretly knew that staff was in charge, but it was important for constituents to believe that their elected official made the decisions.

The function was well populated, filled with real estate agents and construction company executives invited by the Home Builders Institute of America, along with politicians, all attempting to eat and drink and convince each other of their mutual indispensability. There was a feeling of pregnant possibility in the air. Each face was illuminated with the naked hope of potential misconduct; Vegas might have all the glitz and glamour on the surface, but nothing beats Washington for covert inappropriate behavior.

I ultimately found our constituents and engaged them in informed discussion of the state of the region or what John Barry, Dante's minion, called 'Hudson Valley trash talk.' "Yes, new home sales are down but isn't that more a function of the price of oil than any official downturn in the economy? No, I don't think we are heading for a recession even though federal aid to our three most populous cities is dropping like mercury in an upstate nor'easter."

I was exhausted from a day of issues and answers at work and tried to lead the conversation to more salient topics, like where I could recommend they go for dinner or where nightlife was liveliest for middle-aged small business owners from Peekskill or Newburgh. Then I got a tap on the shoulder. I turned to see Representative McLean from Boston granting me the knowing gaze and tantalizing smile that had secured his election three times from his Back Bay neighborhood.

"Just in time," I breathed. "Save me."

"Ladies and gentlemen, allow me to introduce Congressman William McLean from the Commonwealth of Massachusetts."

"I was coming to rescue you," he whispered in my ear, "not entertain your constituents."

I sipped my glass of chardonnay while he went into speech #102 on "The Minimum Wage and its Effect on Small Business." It is known as the art of universal appeal and I couldn't help but admire him, not only for his impeccable appearance but for his ability to win over the men in the audience. Women were naturally drawn to him because of his boyish good looks and perfectly styled hair, but men knew a well manicured phony when they met one and he combated that with a clear grasp of his chosen topics and general air of intelligence. In my view, he fulfilled every childhood fantasy Prince Charming that Disney could draw.

My group disbursed and Will turned to me. "If your top is down, we are taking my car."

"Are you afraid of being seen with me or of messing up your hair?" I half teased.

"I'm not important enough for anyone to notice who I take to dinner."

I smiled. "Maybe I should wait for an invitation from someone more important."

"It is Thursday, May 23rd, if I don't feed you, you won't eat, unless you want to fight for the shrimp over on the far side of the room."

I was both annoyed and amused to realize how well he knew me. Every warning system in my body told me not to fall for this man and I was completely powerless to heed them. The fact that so many were clamoring for his attention and he wanted *me* presented a wave of emotion I couldn't fight. I gave in every time — swept away by his charisma, charm and uncanny ability to exercise infidelity while representing tradition and integrity.

He was good at what he did. He was responsive to his constituents. He was a leader of his peers and the Democratic Party. He had paid his dues as an Assistant District Attorney assigned to the cases no one else would take. He had worked hard at Boston College so that he could attend Harvard Law School and broaden his chances for collective acceptance and admiration. He had married a woman he met in law school who had a successful practice at a blue blood firm in Boston and they were considered the happiest couple in the world. She never came to Washington and he never asked her to accompany him to political functions in his congressional district, but they photographed well in the annual Christmas card and lived the myth of mutual regard.

When Will confessed all of this to me, I was unimpressed. The Hill is a famous breeding ground for older male Congressman/younger female staff relationships, and I was way too smart to fall into that trap. Besides, I went to Vassar and we only dated Yale guys. He laughed with complete abandon when I told him this and said that his Catholic working class family from South Boston would be so impressed that he knew a Vassar girl; not that he graduated from Harvard, not that he was a member of Congress, not that he sat on a committee with jurisdiction over agencies with multi-million dollar budgets and sweeping policies, but that *he knew a Vassar girl.* And this was why I fell for him. He was seemingly unaffected by all that could corrupt his unblemished altar boy essence and if it was my naiveté that kept me from following the seventh commandment, I was sure that on some purer plane of reality and truth, I was not committing any sin but succumbing to the most elemental form of human attraction and desire.

At dinner he would consider me with his azure eyes, expectant and engaged, and I would gaze with the adoration of a Magi at his blond hair, quick smile, clever wit and languid pose, so relaxed and comfortable. His features weren't perfect but like mine, when put together, they added up to an annotated kind of beauty both appreciated and coveted. We talked of work and life and histories and yet despite my stupor, I could not completely block out the reality of our situation. At times I felt completely happy, lucky to have him for a minute or a night, but on the whole I cursed myself for not having a normal, available boyfriend my age.

"What's happening up in Boston?" I would ask, or, "When are you going home?" At this point he would usually give me a sobering look, ask for the check and the magic so prevalent in the early part of the evening would dissipate like the mist rising off of the Potomac on a winter morning.

My black mood, as usual, would not lift. "Please drop me at home."

And when we got to my cobblestone street named after a letter in the alphabet, he would turn to me with those perfectly proportioned features and sky blue eyes and say, "Pari, I am a forty-year-old lawyer from Boston with youth behind me. You are a twenty-four-year-old, beautiful, smart girl from New York. Don't consider me the best you can do." At that point I would close my eyes and feel the weight of his words. Sincere or not, he was humbling himself before me, and it was my choice to reject or accept this powerful man reweighing the scales in my favor. In those moments I thought of my childhood, my family, the plans I had made to run for office myself. I came from elected officials and government consultants on my father's side and I was determined to be the first person in Congress to say that her Grandfather had been a consultant to the Shah of Iran. Ever since the American hostages were taken from our embassy in Tehran in 1979, I was on a one-woman crusade to prove that everyone of Persian descent was not the enemy.

When he reached over to kiss me goodnight, I put his lapel in my fist and pulled him closer. "I will accept you as you are," I whispered, "as long as you concede that the Yankees will always be better than the Red Sox."

❖

My High School graduation, Pine Crest School, Ft. Lauderdale, FLA, 1976

Yankees and Foreigners

The truth is I am not exactly from New York. I certainly lived there most of my life and went to college there, but I was born in California, went to prep school in Florida and while my mother can boast of ancestral ties to early New England, my father came over on the plane, not the boat. The summer my mother took some courses at Barnard, they met, and my father abandoned ideas of medical school

32

for a degree in chemical engineering at Columbia in order to stay in New York with her, and the rest is my biological history.

My father arrived in this country, sent by *his* father, an advisor to the Shah, a Western educated king, who charged the scientifically advanced offspring of the Iranian bourgeoisie to become doctors and lawyers and business-men and then return to Iran to introduce the miracles and conventions of Western learning.

There is an old black and white photograph, yellowing around the edges and wrinkled with age, of the thirty or so Persian students studying in the U.S., meeting with the young Shah Mohammed Reza Pahlavi in a sitting room at Columbia in 1950. My father is there, distinguished by his good looks, puff of thick black hair, and deep brown eyes. I wonder how many stayed in this country, becoming part of the mainstream immigrant culture and how many went back to spread their fresh, American knowledge in the everyday lives of an ancient civilization.

When my father spoke Farsi, I felt special and unique. After all, the Persians can boast many accomplishments in the arts and sciences, not to mention one of the oldest civilizations on earth. My sisters and I visited Iran in 1968 and spent several months rejecting the food and complaining but in truth, it was a rarified moment, embraced so completely by people both foreign and familiar.

During our 1968 holiday in Iran there was a party for us at a different relative's house every night. They were celebrating my father's homecoming after twenty years in the United States, during which time he had gone to prep school, college, graduate school, gotten married to an

American, gotten a job in San Francisco, had three children and moved to New York. Needless to say, he had changed slightly since they saw him last and they were not going to miss this opportunity to fete his triumphant return with his daughters. It took him exactly one week to succumb to the fatigue of too much food and partying.

The tables were always piled with platters of Persian delicacies, enough for ten times the number invited: *borani-e Bademjan*, eggplant and yogurt dip; *kufteh*, herb meatballs in tomato-plum sauce; *juleh kabab*, spiced chicken and tomato kebabs; *shirin polow*, Iranian rice pilaf studded with orange rind and pistachios and crisped with golden rice crust called *tadig*.

Rooms were crammed with children, adults, all somehow related to us by blood or friendship. For a culture that doesn't usually imbibe in alcohol, there was champagne, vodka, scotch and, of course, French wine.

What struck me so abruptly and what will always stay with me, was everyone's cheerfulness. They were delighted to see us, thrilled to be a part of the celebration and genuinely merry. People told jokes and laughed and danced with abandon and joy. At the end of an evening, my cheeks would burn from smiling constantly at all those who could care less if I was an A student or a complete failure. "You are a part of this family," I was sure they were thinking, "and that makes you special and loved."

Even people we saw on the street — shop assistants, clerks — seemed delighted to meet us, honored to greet Americans. I decided this was the most accommodating culture on earth and if I ever felt depressed or overwhelmed I would just need to find some Persians, make tea, bring out the pistachios and engage in a conversation that would invariably strike outsiders as very loud but truly diverting.

When we walked into the massive dining room of my uncle's house to begin yet another night of celebratory feasting, the table was laden with a mountain of rice, twenty or so dishes of questionable origin and a cooked lamb, whose head was presented for eating on a different platter. My three male cousins were all toddlers and therefore destructive. We were given the job of making sure they didn't break anything.

My little cousin, Sahand, took my hand and led me to the roof of the house that was designed as a beautiful garden and terrace. The night was warm and clear and even though we had a significant language barrier, he sat me down and motioned up to the sky with his little hands. He was asking me to look at the stars and we sat there for several minutes in silence, heads tilted and gazing at the heavens. I considered this interlude with quiet under-standing. He was telling me without words, despite the language barrier, that we share the same sky; that even though our worlds are thousands of miles apart, and we could not even have the simplest conversation, we have a bond of similarity that forges our ties and determines our destiny: I felt the hold of family, strong and sturdy.

During the first Shah Pahlavi's rule from 1925-1941, one of his earliest reforms was to decree that all families have a last name. Previously, a person was known as the son of, or even *the son of-the son of-the son of* with three or four first names preceding his own. When my grandfather acquiesced to this directive and decided to take the name Forood from a grand warrior in the Persian epic, *Shahnameh*, some family members protested this move toward modernization and embrace of Western culture but the Shah prevailed, and last names were incorporated into Persian society.

My name is the introduction to my foreignness: during my college years I received invitations to a Christmas Cotillion in New York City addressed to Perry Forwood. Someone must have seen my name on the list and decided that it was drastically misspelled. I never felt sorry that it wasn't Susan or Sarah. Because of my mother's coloring, I don't look particularly foreign. With light brown hair, medium height and medium build, I look like a typical American mix of about eight different cultures. But the eyes never lie and mine are large, almond shaped and dark green with lashes both top and bottom that are long enough to trap dust. And if you really look into my face, you can discern a trait, an ancient flavor, savored and preserved in the visage of my family and passed down for generations from a people who started the world.

During my childhood we spent a great deal of time with my mother's family. It was like having the best of both worlds — exotic and domestic, unusual and normal. When asked if my name had a particular meaning, my mother would blithely reply, "Oh yes! It means angel." A *Peri* is a benevolent fairy spirit or sprite in Persian literature, Indian folklore, Pakistani and Afghani stories — close enough. Our maternal grandmother — white haired, pale and of Scottish ancestry — turned to us and marveled at our tanned skin. "I can't believe you belong to me!" she remarked.

My sisters and I frequently encountered this type of duality. The Forood girls who didn't look or sound foreign were different or special somehow. "They've been half way around the world to Iran! They've tasted unusual food! They can't converse with their Iranian relatives and their mother is blonde and from Philadelphia!"

For my father in the 1950's, everything about America was fresh and fascinating. He could embrace the distinction with his past, or try to reject it but he could not ignore it as it presented itself in a thousand different ways every day. To become American was to grip the dream with both hands, ensuring his place in the rosy future of this ascendant superpower and hang on for the ride. And twenty years later, we, his daughters, were the embodiment of his struggle, running around in that wonderland known as suburbia, shoeless, floating just above the ground, brash with the bravado of first generation amalgamation.

To my immigrant parent, his children were the barometer of success, more so than his personal achievements. If he could look to his offspring as accomplished, integrated members of his adopted culture, he could feel the peace associated with making the decision of leaving his homeland in the first place.

In 1976, I was part of an idealistic group of Baby Boomers, graduating from high school in a bicentennial year filled with hope and good, purposeful intentions. Everything new and undiscovered had an air of mystery and desirability about it. We headed off to college and university knowing that we were a working part of the greatest experiment in representative government history — well-educated, trained and ready to promote that intangible *Americanness* anywhere in the world. We were winning the Cold War, influencing and exploiting the Third World, and feeling the power in the privilege and knowledge of our economic superiority.

In college, professors were fascinated with my background and I was often asked to comment on some aspect of Middle Eastern policy. Since I was not privy to National Security Council briefings at the time, my expertise was limited to the New York Times like everyone else; however, it amused and complimented me. I recall a debate in a political science seminar my junior year about Israeli/Palestinian rights. The professor assigned me the job of leading the Israeli team. He thought he was being provocative whereas I had always been sympathetic to Israel's position in a hostile environment. During the course of the discussion I informed the surprised class, that certain members of the Iranian military were trained in Israel, injecting the thought-provoking fact that Iran was not an Arab state and did not have a history of aggression toward Israel.

I was experiencing a reaction to my surname and ancestry. The fact that the result sometimes led to special treatment softened the blow but it made me realize that people were going to make certain value judgments about me based on my name, look and background. I majored in American politics, specifically the early formation of the U.S. government and constitutional law, with a long distance view toward law school and public service. And whether I realized it or not, I represented the imperfect embodiment of modern America; a success story from the prolific melting pot that fermented a population of half-breeds and quarter-breeds, proving Darwinian Theory of strength in diversity. With these multi-ethnic elements, loyalties were fractured but patriotism was firm.

Few people from the Middle East were moving to the United States in the 1960's and 1970's, and those who did were well-heeled cosmopolitan professionals who were seen to add to the intellectual range of American society.

And then, on November 4, 1979, one day after my twenty-first birthday, members of the American embassy in Tehran were taken hostage and the Islamic Republic of Iran was born. Overnight the country of my ancestors became the enemy and any benign exoticism I felt was lost in the televised video of Americans being led blindfolded to their torture by men who looked like my relatives.

❖

Somewhere Between Iran and Pakistan

When Sahand woke up, cramped and disoriented, he considered his surroundings. He wished he had a bottle opener to help himself to one of the hundreds of bottles of soda serving as his companions. Through the slits in the sides of the truck he could tell it was dusk as they approached the desert. He was thirsty, hungry and hot and about to bang on the wall dividing the cargo from the driver when the truck pulled over and came to an abrupt stop. The driver got out and Sahand could hear voices. He recognized the driver's voice as he had spoken to the man when he stopped around noon to allow Sahand a bathroom break and some water. The driver didn't say much but since he had collected only half of his payment, he knew he had to deliver Sahand to the Pakistani border safely and therefore treated this human freight with a degree of respect.

The present conversation was muted but Sahand could tell it was an argument about money. The two men were haggling over the price of the vehicle's contents or some other pending delivery. Before he could make sense of the dialogue, the back door opened and he sank deeper into the rows of bottles around him. The driver shouted his name. He didn't move a muscle.

"Come out!" the second man shouted.

Sahand's heart froze in his chest. *Please let him be speaking to someone else*, he thought.

"I know you are in there, come out now!" the speaker was adamant and Sahand pictured him with a gun, probably a Kalashnikov, strapped to his chest like the ones issued to soldiers going to Iraq. There was no escape. He was trapped like a cornered mouse and sweat soaked his shirt.

Slowly he stood, hands raised to show he had no weapon. *I think I would rather die here alone than at the Iraqi border,* he thought and raised himself to his full height grimacing at the pain that the stretch caused in his back and legs.

When his eyes adjusted he saw an older man, shabbily dressed, unarmed and bald. His surprise must have registered on his face because the man smirked and then gestured with tired arms for Sahand to climb out of the truck.

As he made his way stepping over bottles and wooden crates, the two men continued to exchange words and Sahand realized they were disagreeing over him.

"I keep the money the father gave to me, and you take him to the border and across and he will pay you the rest," the driver was telling the older man.

"My portion of the journey is more dangerous," the second man shouted. "I deserve more of the money!"

Sahand interrupted the men, "What are you talking about? The understanding was that I am to go the entire distance in this truck, from Tehran to Karachi."

The two men looked at each other and then back at the neophyte outlaw.

"I take you this far, Azim takes you across the border." The truck driver spoke with the abrupt quality of someone who never says more than he has to. Sahand was about to argue when he saw another vehicle nearby.

"Can I ride in the front of your truck in a proper seat until daybreak?"

Azim looked at the first driver who happened to be his brother-in-law and emitted a mirthless laugh. He looked back at the young, hopeful fugitive and pointed at a place five hundred feet away where in the dusk they could barely make out a slight movement next to some small brush. Heat rose off of the ground blurring their vision and causing the air to vibrate. As his gaze expanded to include the entire vista, Sahand saw the arid sand stretching in small waves and reaching to the horizon and beyond with rivulets and gulleys like an ocean of crushed rock. When he moved closer to the spot Azim was pointing out, he saw two large animals poised in the languid stance only camels can achieve. They seemed to be chewing, although in this part of the desert, there was no vegetation for miles.

"You can sit anywhere you like," Azim told him, "as long as it is on top of the camel's back."

Sahand looked away from the two men who were laughing at his expense to the setting sun. He wanted to laugh and cry at the same time. Alive with indignation he wanted to shout to the darkening sky that this was unfair, that he did not deserve this foul fate. Every fiber of his being was breaking apart in frustration and yet through sheer force of will, he kept himself upright and calm. With a purpose he did not feel, he walked toward the camels.

Foroods have been riding camels for centuries, he reasoned, *I need to look like I know what I am doing. If the driver and his brother think I am weak, they will cheat me.*

He turned back to the two men and spoke with authority, "I will give you the other half of the money, but we must leave now. I want to get to the Pakistani border at dawn when the guards are tired and foggy with sleep."

The two men, spent from their show of laughter, looked at each other for a prolonged moment, shared an unspoken agreement and parted.

"He will either get there or he won't. It is in Allah's magnificent hands." Azim followed his customer to the lip of the vast expanse of sand.

My grandmother, Ashraf Forood, daughter of Zadar Rashid,
Provincial Governor of Tabriz

A Short but Important History Lesson

Persian fairy tales begin with the phrase, "There was one
and there wasn't one; except for God, there was no one."
This is their version of "Once upon a time." When I was
small, the bible stories I learned in Sunday school had the
tone and tempo of fairy tales, the clear demarcation
between good and evil and the essential morality lesson.
Whether you believed them or not was immaterial — the
point was to be inspired or chastised or at best, enlightened.

Religious stories answer the questions most pressing to emerging minds: what happens when you die? Is there a God? Did they eat peanut butter in ancient times? If I'm mean to my sister will the devil take me to hell? The parables are comforting for casual believers, fanciful to non-believers, and gospel to those with great faith.

There was one and there wasn't one; except for God, there was no one . . .

In 610 A.D. at the age of forty, Muhammad ibn Abdallah was contemplating his life in a cave on Mt. Hira near his home in Mecca, when an angel appeared to him and spoke the words of God. Since he often went to this holy place to meditate, he was shaken but not shocked by the visitation. The voice called on him to assume leadership of his people and teach them to live their lives closer to God. Muhammad, who initially questioned the veracity of the message, finally listened to the pronouncements urging him to preach mercy for the poor, humanity for those in servitude and to outlaw polytheism. The voice declared itself the one true God, the same one that Jews and Christians worshipped; however, Jesus Christ was not his son, just a prophet whose word was now replaced by this new prophecy, *Islam.*

Muhammad began to preach this new gospel and was chased out of Mecca. He and his followers went to Yathrib also known as Medina, a city filled with Jews and Christians. Since he was preaching monotheism and the dissolution of all pagan idols, the three religions coexisted for a time. And then, with the inevitability of secular conflict, war broke out. In 627 A.D., after a heated battle in Medina, Muhammad had seven hundred Jews beheaded. Three years later, he and his followers conquered Mecca, destroying hundreds of statues of pagan idolatry at the city's great temple of Kabah. He declared Allah the one true God and proclaimed the supremacy of Islam sending messengers to the neighboring countries of Persia, Byzantium, Yemen and Ethiopia urging them to convert.

After Muhammad's death, the record of God's decrees, spoken to him on Mt. Hira, were collected in the Qur'an and the testimonies of his followers, in the Hadith. Islam spread like a virulent rumor to Syria, Egypt, North Africa, Anatolia, Iraq and Persia and in the 8th century, even to Europe when the Muslims invaded the Iberian Peninsula, modern day Spain.

The Sunni and the Shiite sects of Islam have been enemies since they divided over 1,400 years ago. Both recognize and live by the five pillars of Islam: daily prayer; fasting during Ramadan; alms giving; the pilgrimage to Mecca; and belief in one, unitary god. Both sects believe that the Qur'an is the sacred text, that Muhammad was the prophet and that there will be a resurrection followed by a final judgment when the world ends.

The split in Islam started with a fight over who should lead the faithful after the Prophet Muhammad's death in 632. One side believed that direct descendants of the prophet should take up the mantle of the caliph, the leader of the world's faithful. They were known as the Shiat-Ali, or "partisans of Ali," after the prophet's cousin and son-in-law, whom they favored to become their leader. In time, they came simply to be known as Shiites.

The Sunnis thought any worthy man could lead the faithful regardless of lineage, and favored Abu Bakr, an early convert to Islam who had married into Muhammad's family. "Sunni" is derived from the Arab word for "followers" and short for "followers of the prophet."

Sunnis dominated the medieval caliphate and the Ottoman Empire, and Shiites traditionally have been regarded as outsiders. The Shiites were the eventual losers in a violent struggle for leadership that lasted decades, a fact now reflected in their minority status within global Islam. Worldwide, there are about 1.6 billion Muslims; ninety percent are Sunni, but Shiites are a majority in Iran, Syria and Bahrain and the largest Muslim group in Lebanon. The Sunnis populate Jordan, Egypt, Saudi Arabia and include followers of Saddam Hussein in Iraq and Al Qaeda.

Iran, or Persia as it was known until 1935, is one of the oldest continuous civilizations in the world dating back to 4000 B.C.E. Countless dynasties and shahs, or kings, ruled the borderless landmass about the size of Alaska and depending on the conqueror, left their mark on Persian culture. However, in 1550, the Safavid Dynasty took over and established Shiite Islam as the national faith, thus unifying the country under one religion. Islam was widespread by this time and was represented in some of the largest and most influential empires of the 16th and 17th centuries.

The Islamic religion requires daily reading of the Qur'an; therefore, literacy was encouraged among the male population, and as a result, the academic exchange of information and intellectual pursuits grew in Persia in the 17th century. Agricultural and urban infrastructure innovations flourished during the period 1500-1800 and Islamic countries rivaled their European counterparts for technological advancement. Centers of culture and science produced mathematicians, philosophers, astronomers, and physicians as well as musicians and writers during this time of high productivity and wellbeing.

Iran did not attract world attention until World War I when the British, seeking to secure a foothold in the oil rich country, helped engineer a coup d'état led by an officer of the Persian Cossack Brigade, Reza Pahlavi, in 1925. When Reza Shah, the first Pahlavi king, came to power after overthrowing the ruling monarch, he incarcerated the influential mullahs, or priests, and secularized every aspect of Persian society. He did more to Westernize Iran in twenty years than any Middle Eastern leader before or since, bringing it to a level of industrialized sophistication.

Reza Shah introduced many reforms including reorganizing the army, government administration and finances. He abolished all special rights granted to foreigners, thus gaining real independence for Iran. Under his rule, the Trans-Iranian railroad was built, the University of Tehran was established and oil production was restructured and increased — modernization, some say, created at the expense of alienating his people from their ancient religion and culture. During World War II, his relationship with the Germans was protested by the Allies, and in 1941, British and Russian forces invaded and occupied Iran. Reza Shah was forced to abdicate in favor of his son, Muhammad Reza Shah, and he eventually died in exile in South Africa.

His son was a product of his pro-Western leanings. Muhammad Reza was sent to a Swiss boarding school and returned to Iran in his late teens fluent in four languages and completely comfortable with Western culture. Of the two Pahlavi kings, father and son, it is hard to say who promoted the West more.

Muhammad Reza Shah, who ruled the country from 1941-1979, followed his father's grand design and decided that the new Persian identity should conform to Western ideals. He instigated reforms aimed at bringing ancient cultural and religious traditions more in line with western standards of conduct. In the 1960's, a new calendar was introduced with Persian festivals and holidays to the exclusion of Islamic celebrations. Western dress was encouraged and the chador or headscarf worn by Islamic women was banned.

The Shah was viewed by his detractors as a pro-Western puppet whose laws and demands estranged most of his people who were forced to re-examine their own beliefs after being bombarded with Western customs and styles. In retrospect, a revolution and subsequent theocracy was probably brewing in Iran since the first Pahlavi king seized power.

There are many theories explaining the Islamic Revolution in Iran. Simply stated, fifty years of repression by both Pahlavi Kings had stirred up enough resentment to allow a charismatic leader in the form of the Imam, or Holy Leader, Ayatollah Khomeini, to revive a fervency of spirit and fanaticism resulting in anarchy by a willing and agitated young male populace. This virulent minority succeeded in revving up the engine of disaffection, fomenting regime change and hurdling over a stable middle class unprepared for the ruthless quality of hostile reform.

My grandfather, as well as most of the Iranian bourgeoisie influenced by the first Shah Pahlavi, adopted Western customs early. He was delighted to introduce

French food, British wool clothing and American automobiles into his household. Since religion had never been a part of his daily routine, he did not miss it when tiresome Islamic rituals were outlawed, and he agreed with Reza Shah in 1925 when he secularized public education by taking it out of the hands of the mullahs. This one reform did more to Westernize Iran than any other. When a theocracy was established after the Islamic Revolution in 1979, one of the first laws enacted was to bring Islam back into all aspects of public education.

In 1930, my grandfather was sent by his king and boss to Paris to attend the *École Militaire,* or French Military College. My uncle and my father spent their earliest years in Paris with their parents propagating and fostering a love of France and French customs that lasted their entire lives. When they returned to Iran, French furniture, clothing and a nanny accompanied them. They knew of America, of course, but it wasn't until after WWII that the ancient world realized the importance and far-reaching influence of the United States and guessed at its impending global dominance.

It must have been a bold decision in 1947 to send my father to school in America rather than to France. My uncle was in France in boarding school and years later my grandparents would send their youngest child to Switzerland to a French-speaking school as well, but my father, a precocious teenager with good looks and bad habits, was given the opportunity to sink or swim in what must have seemed the uncharted territory of the final frontier.

At the time no one gave my grandfather credit, but I think he showed great perception in his resolve concerning his second son's future. From that one random and maybe even prophetic decision, he paved the way for the next generation to bask in freedom and prospective prosperity. Of his eight grandchildren, all were educated in the U.S.; six of us live here, the other two in Europe.

My grandmother is the only one I now associate with Islam. She was the oldest of four sisters and one brother and the daughter of a provincial Governor of Iran. I remember disjointed things about her from my first and lasting impressions during our trip to Iran in the summer of 1968: the look of love in her eyes when she gazed on her granddaughters for the first time; the emotional reunion with my father after sixteen years; the way her head shook slightly with Parkinson's disease; her reverent posture as she knelt facing East on her prayer rug every morning and afternoon.

Years later she came to the U.S. for her cataract operation when I was in my teens, and stayed at my father's house cooking and rearranging his possessions. She liked to make a rice pudding dessert for me called *sholeh zard*. It is made with basmati rice (rinsed four or five times), rose water and saffron rendering it almost more fragrant than tasteful, and she sprinkled the cinnamon and nutmeg mixture on the top in what I thought was an indistinguishable design but what I later learned was my name written in Farsi. She was kindness personified with soft brown hair and eyes that saw the world as something to be accepted and tolerated. She did not speak English so we couldn't converse but she smiled broadly whenever I looked at her and constantly encouraged me to eat during every waking hour.

At one point, I found her washing her clothes in the bathtub and tried to communicate through a type of sign language that I would teach her to use the washing machine but she just shook her head. When I asked my father to help her, he regarded me with resignation and told me that she would not put her belongings in the same machine with the clothes of non-believers.

In old photos she looks regal. She was, after all, the eldest daughter of a Governor and enjoyed wealth and prestige in her youth. As a child she was taught to read the Qur'an and memorize its lessons and teachings. Even though she allowed her religion to lapse when she lived in France, she returned to it, fulfilling the duty of the pilgrimage, or hajj, to Mecca in her seventies.

Despite Reza Shah's declarations banning the old religious rituals, her mother, my great-grandmother held court in her home periodically, inviting whichever mullah was most popular to speak at her salons on various subjects in the Qur'an. No one questioned her right to host these soirees, because she was a widow and led a quiet life as dictated by her faith, and her pedigree was considered above reproach. She grew up with rich Islamic traditions as part of her daily life before the advent of the Pahlavi Dynasty, and considered the recitation of prayers and the celebration of holidays, fasts and feasts, as old habits without rancor and above politics. Her eldest daughter, my grandmother, influenced by her mother's character and customs, found comfort with the involuntary gestures and ministrations of the ancient ways. She prayed to Mecca, fasted during Ramadan and covered her head with a silk scarf when appropriate.

As I sit in my small Episcopal church where I was christened and confirmed, I wonder about religion's influences. I do not consider myself deeply devout and yet I sense a certain spirituality in my character which allows me to accept the unexplainable or disprovable in most faiths. To have faith in fate — that is an eastern trait and it suffuses my actions and outlook. When Madeleine Albright, our first woman Secretary of State, learned as an adult that her parents were war refugees and that she was Jewish, she was understandably shocked but resigned. "I have been a Catholic and an Episcopalian and found out I was Jewish," she said. "Like America, I am indivisible."

I know how she feels. I am the granddaughter of Congregationalists, part of the original Protestants settling this country on my mother's side, and on my father's side, I am descended from the followers of Muhammad.

❖

Night Prophecy

"I am exhausted and all I want to do is sit on this couch and stare out the window at traffic, trees, time." I trailed off lost in thought.

"You shouldn't be so tired!" Will laughed at me, "this is an early night for us — House in recess at 5:00 thanks to the Speaker's sciatica and only one tiring reception in the Cannon Caucus Room filled to capacity with Daughters of the American Revolution." He was smiling while he looked dismissively through his mail. The important pieces went to Boston.

"I could be a member of that organization, you know," I told him as a surprising matter of fact.

He stopped reading mail and looked at me. "You?! My benign fairy sprite from Persian folklore with olive skin and deep green eyes the size of saucers? I'm sad to hear it. You are much more interesting with the mixed blood of your far flung ancestors."

I smiled at his objection. "Are you calling me a mutt? I will have you know that as the third daughter of the second son of the first daughter I am entitled to a title!"

He laughed at my convoluted explanation. "In that case, Princess Pari, I am going downstairs to work out in the gym, so that your highness can rest."

Will's apartment was functional, comfortable, generic. He rented it furnished from some Member of Congress defeated long ago and morphed into a lawyer/lobbyist who could now afford a big house on Massachusetts Avenue next to the Peruvian Embassy. I was grateful for the lack of photographs and domestic touches that would have made it difficult to rest my gaze.

I stared until my eyes weren't looking at anything anymore. They must have closed when I fell asleep because I remember the unsettling dream that descended quickly on my mind. My grandfather was speaking to me, earnestly, imploringly, hands gesticulating wildly, urging me to understand, and I couldn't, of course, because he was speaking Farsi. We were sitting in his house in Shemron, a suburb of Tehran, in a room where we used to drink tea and relax that summer in 1968 when I was eight years old, the only time I was ever there.

But in this dream, I was older, my present age and he was trying to explain something important to me. For all I knew it could have been the history of *takhteh nard,* or backgammon, which the Persians invented and play on an elaborately carved wooden board with ivory dice. During our visit to Iran, the language barrier was too strong and the only real interaction we had with my grandfather was when he taught us to play. Because of his enthusiasm I learned my first words of Farsi — *jof panj* and *jof sheesh,* meaning double fives and double sixes. Or in my dream he could have been telling me his reason for sending my father to the U.S. when everyone else in the Iranian bourgeoisie was sending their children to Europe to be educated, or considering his intonation, it could have been his ultimate confession.

He was not devout, and even if he had been affected by his early schooling, Muslims do not believe in confessing their sins to anyone but God, or Allah. But the end of life brings with it the universal necessity to unburden the soul and he was desperately trying to tell me something. I had heard of his many indiscretions, mostly involving his children's nannies or female house servants. When he and his family lived in Paris during my father's very young childhood, the rumors that he gambled away my grandmother's inherited jewels in Monte Carlo were family folklore. The first time I heard this I thought, *No wonder my grandmother left him; I would have had him arrested!* But the strict laws of marriage or female indentured servitude in Muslim countries forbade her from doing anything but moving in with her sister after the children went to boarding school.

Grandfather, are you explaining yourself to me, your granddaughter? Are you justifying your actions or begging for forgiveness, seeking some form of atonement? If there is no heaven or Paradise when we die, then our descendants and their memory is all we have to immortalize us. Wasn't it Pericles who said, "Once we die, what we leave behind is not what is engraved in stone monuments, but what is woven into the lives of others?"

I am colorful, grandfather. I am interesting and multicultural and introspective all because of my ancestors and who they were and where I come from. The United States is a land of immigrants, just as you imagined it, made rich and diverse by our dissimilar origins complimenting and converging on a stage of spontaneous interaction. You were right to send your son here. It may have been your greatest decision. Rest easy, we will infuse your memory with the tapestried truths of our imperfect recollections. Never fear, you are immortal in our eyes, we will always remember you.

And after all what is memory but the attempt to explain and understand the present.

I awoke to find Will sitting on the couch next to my waist, gazing down at me. When I opened my eyes he came into focus like the slow discovery of a lost object.

"I must have dozed off," I said.

"You must have been dreaming; your face was one wild contortion!" he was looking at me with worry and I was grateful for his concern.

I half rose to hug him, relieved to understand the language someone was speaking to me.

"You smell great," I whispered in his ear.

"I exercised and showered," he replied.

"Clean, cool and crisp, just like freshly washed lettuce." I hugged him harder.

"And you," he muttered into my neck, "are warm and soft and bubbling like a multi-layered casserole."

We kissed, the extremes meeting and releasing their mutual need.

"I fear thy passion doth match my own," I told him in broken Shakespeare.

"Dear Lady, my passion far exceeds yours in all bounds, material and immaterial, terrestrial and celestial, shouted and uttered."

Alas, a semantic contest.

"Impossible Kind Sir," I countered, "for I am vested body and soul despite the overt objections of my ancestors who just spoke to me from beyond the grave."

"It will be my life's quest to prove worthy to your ancestors from near and afar, here and beyond," he murmured.

Yes, we will be tested. That's what my grandfather was trying to tell me — of the epic task we would all be given and its reverberations over time.

❖

The Problem Presents Itself

"Pari, it's your father on line two."

I looked up from the New York Times. It was either 6:45 a.m. in San Francisco or 3:45 p.m. in Paris. I could never keep track of where he was. After my parents' divorce, my father moved back to San Francisco and then ran Chevron offices in Europe. He had been in Brussels for a number of years and then Paris and if his French was good before, now it was perfect. He picked up languages quickly and always said that English was the toughest to learn.

"O-u-g-h can be pronounced so many different ways!" he would complain. "Like "f" in rough; like "u" in through; like "o" in though; or "aw" in thought — what kind of language is this?!"

That used to make me laugh and feel slightly superior. I had no trouble navigating these words, even at an early age. My sisters and I spent our childhood correcting his English to our delight, but his grasp of math and science transcended language barriers and he graduated with honors and distinction in his fields of chemistry and chemical engineering, all subjects I never found compelling.

Having a parent whose first language was not English gave me the obnoxious habit of finishing people's sentences, whether they were foreign or not. Seeing my father struggle to find a word jump-started my competitive nature and before anyone else could supply it, I would blurt out two or three options and he would calmly pick the one that best fit what he was trying to say. I would mentally reward myself a gold star and listen attentively for the next opportunity.

According to my father, the perfect American family sat at the dinner table every night and discussed events of the day. They were erudite, animated and engaged, beautifully dressed and coiffed, healthy and fit. He must have read somewhere that Joe Kennedy ruled over his evening repast successfully creating senators and presidents and philanthropists.

Our dinner tables were slightly different.

After soliciting monosyllabic replies from us about our day at school, we would settle into the mundane act of eating fast so that we could be excused to retreat to our rooms to listen to our favorite Beatles, Turtles, or Monkees album. However, it was an unspoken rule that no one could leave the table until my father had finished eating and he ate more methodically and slower than a toothless man trying to gum a raw steak. He probably thought he was instilling discipline and good eating habits but to this day, I wolf down my food standing up or eating in the car bringing indigestion to a new and impressive level.

"Dad, how are you? How's Nicole? Where are you?"

Even though English was not his first language or the one he spoke on a daily basis, I tended to bombard him with questions forcing his multi-lingual brain to play catch-up. Nicole, his French girlfriend who worked at the American Embassy in Paris, spoke to him in French in the same rapid fashion. He must have felt verbally assaulted every time he spoke to one of us.

"I am in Paris but heading back to San Francisco at the end of the week. I am fine and Nicole sends her love but Pari, I need to be both frank and quick because I am leaving for Brussels this afternoon and I have to go home and pack. I want to talk to you about a situation with your cousin, Sahand."

I tried to picture the two year old guiding me around his dining room table in Iran sixteen years ago.

"He has escaped from Iran in order to avoid serving in the army during this war with Iraq and is on his way to Karachi, Pakistan to purchase a passport so that he can fly to France and then to the U.S.," he explained with extreme severity.

I was stunned into silence, trying to imagine a toddler running from menacing authorities with guns. And then I remembered a more recent photo of a young man with typical teenage brown bangs and shaggy hair at least as tall as HF and felt relief that he would be able to outrun his enemies.

"Why did he have to escape from Iran?" I asked. I was incredulous that someone from my normal middle class family would need to escape from anything but their normal middle class family.

"He received a letter drafting him into the army and his parents decided they could not allow him to be sent to the Iraqi front and possibly killed. So he has been smuggled out of the country and he will hopefully get to Pakistan in two or three days."

"Dad, that's incredible, he's only, what, sixteen, seventeen?" I felt the little hand in mine, so small and animated, when we were on the roof garden looking at the stars at his house in Tehran.

My father continued. "He is seventeen and totally on his own. My brother is frantic, and his wife is inconsolable. Nicole will help on this end but we will need you to get involved."

"What can I do?" I asked.

And now my fate was sealed. Whatever ties, however strong, I felt with my cousins from half a world away were being tested. The battle for who I was officially waged with the reality of who I pretended to be. The days of shrugging at the mail I received addressed to Perry Forwood were brought into stark relief. I am the daughter of a first generation immigrant and my family needs my help. For the immediate future my life would be consumed with navigating this young man's escape through the desert and black market, and through the back alleys and front offices of the official and unofficial course of reaching freedom.

Hamilton Fish, Jr., my father, my mother's sister, Ginia Davis, my mother, Ginia's husband, Morris Wexler

The Big Picture

All roads lead to Washington. Even powerful New York or brainy Chicago or cosmopolitan San Francisco have to go through our nation's Capitol for permission to build a highway, revive a tainted water supply, or at the very least, collect their allowance. Congress holds court every day, accepting visitors like subjects supplicating themselves before the king. Captains of industry, local politicians, sports heroes and foreign dignitaries make their way through the maze of Capitol Hill office buildings with its thousands of support staff running or talking at breakneck speed, rushing to get it done before the vote, before the press conference, before the plane leaves to take the Congressman back to the home district.

To enter this world is to put your dignity at stake — it represents the most ironic imbalance of power in the world: a lobbyist in a $3,000 suit stuffed into a cramped back office trying to educate and persuade a Legislative Aide making $3,000 a month. America's best and brightest, who graduated from Ivy League law schools, working for freshmen Members of Congress whose last job on the local Board of Education or quarterbacking the pro football team, somehow convinced their electorate in Ohio or Florida or Wisconsin that they should represent them in the most important deliberative body in the modern world. The check is to avoid the concentration of responsibility and the balance is to make sure everyone knows it.

My morning commute through Georgetown along Rock Creek Parkway passed the Lincoln Memorial, the Tidal Basin and the Jefferson Memorial, the tens of thousands of tulips planted for Queen Beatrix of the Netherlands when she came to visit or the perfectly pruned cherry trees sent as a present from the people of Japan. From all of these temples strategically situated throughout this iconic city, one can view the gods of American history, tributes to the men who formulated the basis for public policy from grand schemes and borrowed dreams — those who were blissfully unaware of their impact on the prologue of time and therefore fleetingly, uncompromised and unfettered — free of the bonds of temporal responsibility. It is our redeeming quality as Americans, our immaculate conception.

It is the reason Washington takes your breath away: because its birth was based on an ideal. And despite its modern day reduction to the defense of ill-gotten gains and influence peddling and Machiavellian party politics, the core is untouchable. Washington is the embodiment of the premise of human beneficence and resilience, the ascension of the individual and what that one empowered mind can accomplish. It is why we tear up when we sing the national anthem and why millions of people who may not vote or may eschew all politics and politicians, come to visit and make claim to their piece of the dream. It is why every spring it took me forty-five minutes to get to my office as opposed to fifteen minutes at any other time of year.

And yet it is sometimes difficult to be the bearer of that legacy. Our history, lauded and emulated, is also pockmarked with shameless acts of greed and depravity. Our treatment of slaves, Native Americans, all cultures and nationalities new to our shores, has not always been a shining example of ideal behavior. A nation founded by immigrants exercises the intolerance of racism again and again. And the men, some brave and well-meaning, who formed this government with sacred words on prickly parchment couldn't keep their laws from imposing prejudice on anyone but themselves.

Each day we tried to redeem ourselves in meeting after meeting with the underrepresented or the forgotten minority who had been treated unfairly by the huge bureaucracy formed by and for the people. Everyone from the receptionist to the Congressman spent a good part of the time encouraging, placating and apologizing to groups of citizens angry or driven by a desire to be heard. We tried to be efficient, like an office in the private sector, conscious of the bottom line, but our inherent flaws or the sheer magnitude of the problems defied simple solutions.

The hierarchy of a Congressional office is unvaried and respected. Unlike normal business offices, one cannot aspire to be the boss simply by working hard and increasing the profit margin. This relationship tends to grant respect to the elected official and his weighty position. Add to that the indisputable fact that a majority of the people who made it out to the polls on that rainy day in November liked him/her the best and you have the results of the ultimate popularity contest. Complimenting the overall feeling of hushed reverence in the hallowed halls is the reality that the voter back home in Spartanburg or Seattle can simply change their mind and get rid of everyone. We felt powerful, we acted powerfully and yet our history of impermanence is well documented.

Congress is a reactive body; the issue presents itself out in the real world and it is then brought to Capitol Hill as a screaming emergency or a simple grievance or something in between. As a perfect example, immigration policy was failing and the country looked to us to fix it. Temporary worker programs, amnesty for illegal immigrants, tougher border patrols and restrictions — all aspects of it were on the table and all three branches of government were trying to shape reform. We were in the thick of it and the Immigration Subcommittee of the House Judiciary Committee member Will McLean, current heartthrob, was the germination point. It helped that HF was Ranking Minority member (highest ranking Republican) on the subcommittee and full Judiciary Committee as well. If fate was telling me to address this issue on a personal as well as professional level, I was getting the message.

Young people drawn to Washington and government service, especially those working in the House and Senate are special at best or self-destructive at worst. They are motivated by a sense of duty and maybe even a smattering of patriotism but there is a reason they want to be a part of the solution. I saw it every day in the weary yet resolute faces of staff trying to solve a problem or right the ship of state when it went off course.

I championed many causes for the good of a group or an individual. At the end of the day, if I didn't feel like I helped someone or illuminated some indecipherable federal puzzle or explained a new initiative designed to address a problem, then my time was wasted. Congressional staff, the unelected policy-influencers, were the warriors on the front lines of representative democracy, fighting for the people, and winning a few battles but mostly trying to keep our heads above the churning waters of an ever-growing public sector that grew more impersonal with each passing day. We weren't better or more noble than our private sector counterparts; however, a good deal of self-sacrifice came with our job and our metaphorical blood was spilt each time we lost our heart to a constituent who needed us.

Taking on my cousin's plight was my bread and butter. Even as a Press Secretary, I dove into the mess that was constituent service on a weekly basis and attempted to be helpful or right a wrong or explain the maze of the federal process to outsiders. I remember the time a constituent came down to Washington to persuade us to support a bill to fund research for a disease afflicting his son. Judiciary Committee was in full session and the other legislative staff was swamped. I saw his face fall slightly when he was told he would be meeting with the Press Secretary as opposed to someone with jurisdiction over healthcare legislation or better still, the Congressman, but he soldiered on and explained the issue to me and when he was done, he gathered up his briefcase with all of its supporting documentation, thanked me for my time, and left. I wrote a short memo for the Congressman on the meeting, and when, through no influence of ours, the research was funded in the Health and Human Services Appropriations bill, I wrote to our constituent with the good news. The next day, a florist arrived with a big fichus plant that I was not allowed to accept as it was over the dollar limit for gifts to staff in the House of Representatives.

❖

Paris

The Élysée Palace in Paris, like the White House and Number 10 Downing Street, serves as the residence and workplace of the President of France. The highest ranking staff works in close proximity to the President in the former Empress Eugenie's private apartments.

As Chief of Protocol, Marie Claude Lassurance occupied an office near the Counsel of Ministers' Chamber. Her position carried more weight than the mundane task of organizing official functions for visiting dignitaries. She was the guardian of French history and customs, protecting centuries of tradition from royalty to Robespierre through Napoleonic influence and five Republics.

Marie Claude was from a patrician family. In 1750, when the Marquise de Pompadour purchased what is now the Élysée Palace, she commissioned her favorite architect, Marie Claude's ancestor, to make the necessary renovations. Monsieur Lassurance renovated the structure to suit the mistress of Louis XV and subsequently altered the garden with the introduction of porticos, hedgerows, waterfalls, a maze, and a gilded grotto.

Marie Claude never verbally alluded to her majestic relation; however, her posture and demeanor reeked of entitlement and exclusion. She dismissed those who were inconsequential in her view and coveted those who were worthy. Her manners, character and carriage were as exemplary as her pedigree and when it came to questions of protocol, she was always consulted.

Arriving each morning in couture usually consisting of a Chanel suit and Christian Dior shoes, Marie Claude was punctual and prepared. Her hair was perfectly coiffed at Alexandre de Paris and her makeup was tasteful and complimentary. She was the picture of decorum and President François Mitterrand relied on her to smooth over diplomatic breeches and bumps with aplomb and circumspection, employing what the French refer to as *détente delicat*.

She was efficient but feminine, fair but firm and never tolerated the same mistake twice. To work for her was to sacrifice your self-confidence and ego, to swallow your pride and any retort when being berated for wearing the wrong shoes or the wrong expression. But it was also to be exposed to the grandeur of French functions, to walk in the footsteps of kings, Emperors who defined bravado and intellectual giants who crafted the Age of Reason.

President Mitterrand, the longest serving elected leader in France's history, felt the immense burden of defending this cultural inheritance. He entrusted the responsibility to Marie Claude who in turn took it more seriously than an appointment to the *cour de cassation*, one of France's four Supreme Courts. She loved working for this man and like the rest of the country, looked the other way when he would leave the Élysée Palace, take a long walk, make love to his mistress and kiss his love children on the cheek, all on the way home to his wife and family. His contributions to French culture were grand gestures designed to affirm the general belief that French influence is carried throughout the world on the wings of its chefs, painters, authors and dress designers.

When Marie Claude walked down the hall, no fewer than six people followed at all times. She would bark orders and instructions in rapid-fire fashion earning her nickname, the Howitzer.

"What time does the ambassador arrive?" she spat.

"Where will the press be seated? Who is escorting the First Lady? Who will take care of the transportation? When does the plane touch down?"

All of the details associated with a successful state function were carefully stored in her immaculately styled head of blonde pomp and circumstance.

Her two sons in English boarding school always received preferential treatment when visiting, as did her husband, but they knew that her first love was her position as keeper of France's public face. She acquiesced to the notion that British public school was good for her sons, despite the longstanding feud between the English and the French. She secretly believed that Anglicans were better at disciplining children while the French tended to be soft and indulgent, as illustrated by the difference between a fine French repast that soothed the senses and infused the soul and an English meal that simply sustained the body. She would not have her sons growing up coddled and spoiled. After all, how could they be corporate leaders or senators without the liberal use of the rod of educational discipline?

One morning in May of 1984, Marie Claude perused the three newspapers on her desk, read about the Iran/Iraq war, a threatening transit workers strike in Paris, a new exhibit at the Centre Pompidou, and the weather report for the French Open. She leafed through phone messages and saw one marked urgent from her closest childhood friend. She wondered why Nicole, with whom she had just played tennis last week, needed her immediate attention.

She phoned the American Embassy where Nicole worked as translator. Marie Claude smiled and sat back in her chair when she heard her friend's greeting.

"Nicole, *ça va?*"

"Yes, yes I am fine but I need to talk to you about something important." Nicole half whispered with great urgency.

"If you want tickets to the Opera, it is impossible. I gave mine away to the Japanese ambassador in exchange for his attendance at the State dinner honoring WW II veterans. You know how they hate those functions."

"It is nothing about tickets," assured her friend. "We need help for Bob's nephew who will be arriving from Pakistan with a false passport after illegally escaping from Iran on the back of a camel! He is only seventeen years old and scared to death! Once he gets to France, he will need to get past the border police when he arrives at the airport!"

Marie Claude was too stunned to reply; seconds drifted by in silence.

"Hello, Marie, are you still there?" Nicole ventured carefully.

Finally Marie Claude spoke, "What exactly are you asking me to do?"

Nicole continued, making sure no one was listening. "I have no idea really but I know we need to contact the border police when we get his flight information so that they don't arrest him for traveling with an illegal passport when he lands at Charles de Gaulle from Karachi and I was hoping that an inquiry from the President's office might call them off. Pari, Bob's daughter, will be helping from her office in Washington to get him into the U.S. from France. He won't spend time here, as soon as his travel documents can be obtained from the American embassy, he will be on a flight to California," she assured her friend.

Nicole tended to speak very fast in complex sentences with many phrases and clauses. At times, it was attributed to the qualities associated with her light yellow hair color. She was tall and fit with an athletic build and handsome face that didn't exactly stop traffic but certainly slowed it a bit. And, like any French woman, she dressed with flair and understatement, topping off most outfits with an Hermes scarf and styled *coiffeur*. When she and Marie Claude played doubles together, their tennis skills were overshadowed only by their photogenic appeal.

More silence ensued. Marie Claude was now thinking that her friend was joking. She was honestly hoping that Nicole had fabricated this ridiculous story to amuse and lighten her day and she waited patiently for the punch line. None came.

"Marie, say something!" Nicole implored.

"This is like asking me to move *l'arc de triomphe* to Belgium," Marie Claude deadpanned. "I cannot imagine why you think I can make these types of phone calls, mention the President's name and like magic, whatever I ask for, it's granted. You have been working with the Americans too long."

"It will take one phone call from your office to the border police with a suggestion that someone special is arriving from Karachi and not to look too closely at his travel documents or detain him," Nicole said exasperated.

"That is all you have to do. You know if you promise them special seats at Roland Garros, they will do anything you ask."

"I have requests from everyone to watch the French Open tennis! Those passes are more valuable than reservations at Alain Ducasse right now. Why should I help this person?" Marie Claude stood next to her desk and paced as far as the phone cord would allow.

"He is a good boy." Nicole softened her voice in supplication, thinking of the photo of the tall young man standing with his arms casually but affectionately around the shoulders of his proud parents. "I have not met him but Bob has showed me his letters. Besides, his parents do not want him to die in the war with Iraq! You have sons — you can imagine what you would do to save them from certain death. This seems small when faced with that future."

Marie Claude sighed. "I will see what I can do." Staring absently into space, she pondered the fate of young men, conscripted into wars they did not understand or believe in. *The international political arena uses them like pawns,* she thought, *no wonder everyone was escaping to America. It is 1984, how long will it be before the Americans are drawn into a Middle Eastern conflict and begin sacrificing their own sons and daughters?*

She glanced at a photograph of her children. They too were teenagers — bright, eager, innocent. She walked around her office, shiny black heels sinking into the soft Aubusson carpet, and allowed herself a moment's reprieve from the vigilance of her official duties.

In the lull of her uncharacteristic reverie, redolent with the scent of ancient obligation and fresh cut peonies, her gaze lifted and she was confronted with the painting most associated with the nation and glory of France, *Liberty*

Leading the People, by Delacroix. Capturing a moment from the July Revolution of 1830, it now hung in her office on loan from the Louvre. In its heat and activity, Marie Claude could almost feel the immediacy of the crisis and carnage in this allegorical work. Death is everywhere — raw, unadulterated, uncensored — depicted in prostrate bodies with vacant faces and lifeless limbs. In the foreground, one corpse lies frozen in time, his eyes locked in a betrayed expression, as if faced with the astonishing realization that patriotism and devotion were not enough to save him. *War is hell,* she thought, *whether it's in Iran or the streets of Paris.*

She walked up to the painting, and mimicking one of the Louvre tour guides, explained to the furniture in her office, "This painting is a perfect example of 19th century Romanticism, combining drama, terror, violence and heroism in one sweeping gesture to awaken the crowd's courage and create hope from hopelessness and fear."

She turned to her 'audience' of Louis XVI furniture and continued the tour. "Romantic ideas centered on art as inspiration; the spiritual and aesthetic dimension of nature as metaphors for organic growth. Art, rather than science, Romantics argued, could best express universal truth."

Universal truth. Her mind stuck on the thought. *Name one truth that every nationality, country or religion believe in.* She challenged herself and immediately felt the futility of the task. *There is a boy trying to find his way to safety — one traveler on a journey like so many before him and so many after. Maybe the universal truth is that people will always venture forth for whatever reason — opportunity, security, freedom — on a trackless path of shifting sand to find a place called home.*

Part II

She who would rather die with him

Than live to gain the world beside! —

So quickly do his baleful sighs

Quench all the sweet light of her eyes,

One struggle — and his pain is past —

Her lover is no longer living!

One kiss the maiden gives, one last,

Long kiss, which she expires in giving!

Again the Peri soars above,

Bearing to Heaven that precious sigh

Of pure, self-sacrificing love

But, ah! Even Peri's hopes are vain —

Again the Fates forbade, again

The immortal barrier closed — 'Not yet,'

The Angel said as with regret.

Paradise and the Peri from *Lalla Rookh* (1817)
by Sir Thomas Moore (1779-1852)

❖

Karachi, Pakistan

A Third World city in the Middle East is unlike its
counterpart in the industrialized West. The first thing that
strikes you is the unfamiliar sounds: the chant of the
muezzin calling men to prayer in the mosque; the constant
low and persistent hum — not of animals or insects but of
human activity — base and ordinary and yet indicative of
all that is vital and alive; the blare of car horns mixed with
the hoof beats of horses, cows and oxen. There is an
immediate and overpowering assault on your senses by the
earthy smell of too many bodies living in too small an area.
Activity spills out onto sidewalks and streets and alleyways
blurring the distinction between interior and exterior space;
traditional walls of confinement, private acts of daily ritual,
are smelled, shared, witnessed and dismissed as millions are
preoccupied with the ancient and all-consuming struggle to
survive.

Naji sold English, French, German and Japanese
newspapers, cigarettes and candy on the street in Karachi.
He was tall and stringy with the dark complexion and hair
native to his region, but his gait was erect and proud and he
wore his devotion to Islam like a crown. He would banter
with his customers, bowing with obsequious servitude while

storing his resentment in a practiced demeanor of masked indifference. His western style clothes and clean shaven face put foreigners at ease, but the look deep in his dark eyes betrayed the enmity and distrust of all strangers endemic to his sect.

Despite his discomfort, Naji met and haggled with foreign tourists every day. An International Herald Tribune may cost five dinari to someone in a suit and tie, and two to a young student from the subcontinent. He gravitated toward the consulates instead of hotels where junior officers who had become his regulars got a better deal than higher-grade officials too aloof to learn his name or his country's customs.

In 1947, when imperialist Great Britain agreed to divide its protectorate known as British India, two sovereign states were formed: the Dominion of Pakistan now known as the Islamic Republic of Pakistan, and the Union of India now the Republic of India. Two countries, once joined, split in two along religious lines.

After Partition, as the split was known, when Pakistan became independent, the Hindus of Karachi left for India and were replaced by Urdu-speaking Muslim refugees from British India, called Muhajirs. In order to help them settle and assimilate, the new government gave them the property abandoned by the departing Hindus. The new immigrants quickly became a dominant political majority in the city, much to the consternation of the existing population.

Karachi had been accepting refugees since Alexander the Great camped there to prepare his fleet for the Babylonian campaign in 373 B.C. The present city started life as a fishing village because of its well-situated location on the northern shores of the Arabian Sea west of the Indus

River Delta. By 1899, Karachi was the largest wheat exporting port in the East with approximately 100,000 inhabitants — Hindus, Muslims, Europeans, Jews, Parsis, Persians and Lebanese.

In 1979 during the Soviet War in Afghanistan when Afghan refugees began pouring into Karachi, the immigrant population ballooned by about one million. In 1984, Pashtuns, Tajiks, Uzbeks and Hazaras — tribes of Afghanistan — were added to the Arabs, Iranians, Turkish, Filipinos, Arakani (refugees of Myanmar), Bosniaks, Albanians, Poles, Lebanese, Armenians, Bengalis and African immigrants who found their way to form the total population of this multi-racial city. It was a crossroads for the subcontinent and if you knew where to go and who to ask you could find or purchase anything, especially a passport.

Naji was part of the Muhajirs. He spoke Urdu to his family, but because of the hundreds of languages spoken in Karachi, he could converse or sell his merchandise in about ten others. As a result, he overheard and understood conversations whose speakers were oblivious to his mental acuity. He stored information and sold it like cigarettes. In a city of fourteen million people, all hungry for human necessities, it was incumbent upon him to do anything to sustain his family. Each day he rose at 5:00 a.m. to go to work and stepped over the sleeping bodies of his wife, six children, his wife's widowed sister and her young son. He could not remember the last time he thought about anything but putting food on the table.

Naji met businessmen and consulate officials in small cafes and markets 'by chance' to exchange gossip for cash. It could be as inconsequential as personnel decisions or

78

office equipment purchases or as significant as proposed plots of insurgency. He listened to the French, English, Hebrew, Hindi and Urdu and charged the recipient of the information accordingly.

The foreign officials who sought him were informed of his value by Naji's carefully trained associates who performed menial duties in the consulates and official residences. He controlled a network of men and women who hated all of the intruders and were therefore happy to make money by listening and stealing from them. They fed a constant stream of information that flowed from foreign mouths to domestic ears and transformed into currency along the way. Naji did not realize that on a grand scale he was a factor in the political imbalance in the region and his influence was more powerful than many of those who took him for an inconsequential native.

The highest price for information was extracted from the French, then the Americans and British and then Israel, India and his own country. He did not have an advanced moral compass to determine rates, he was just well aware of the laws of supply and demand and who would pay without attempting to cheat him or haggle.

When he worked at the consulates unloading boxes and hauling away garbage, he memorized the discarded possessions. He would bribe the cleaning men to allow him entry at night so he could peruse the superfluous items that could disappear without notice. No one would miss an ashtray or a box of pencils or consider their trash unsafe from careful examination. He stole, lied and cheated but since it was all affecting nonbelievers, it did not matter.

Naji was confused and angry at all of the foreigners in his country. He often passed on the words 'strategic priority' to his customers and questioned if it really meant anything or if it was just a reason to defend their presence and justify their actions so far from home. He was resourceful, clever and wary and treated every encounter like his last. Always suspicious of all who temporarily trusted him, he ached within from the futility of his Sisyphean existence.

Naji was consumed by the struggle to survive and suffered with a constant hunger nagging in his belly since an abstemious childhood left him permanently unable to assuage an emptiness that clawed at his insides like an ulcer. The will and life force that honed his survival instincts shaped his actions and while others may have viewed his business practices as mundane, they were actually calculating moves designed to extract the essence from every activity and feed off its heart.

Of all his activities, he was most wary of the sale of false passports. It was by far the most lucrative but also the most dangerous. Twice soldiers had raided the small house where the documents were forged, confiscating all the machines and materials, and arresting him and his partners. He and his colleagues had been successful in bribing the judge, who ultimately declared there was "insufficient evidence to prove illegal activity" and they were all free to melt into the swarming city and disappear.

Naji himself was followed and questioned about his close association with foreigners but he only shrugged and explained that he was a stupid seller of newspapers on the streets with no interest in politics. Still, he kept the eyes in the back of his head trained for any suspicious movement and lived in a constant state of hyper-awareness.

In May of 1984, because of the war pitting Iran against Iraq and the soviet occupation of Afghanistan, Pakistan in general and Karachi in particular were unsettled and tense. Naji could feel it in the way people reacted to the heat which rose everyday like a steady drumbeat of unrelenting rhythm. It played in his ears with such power until deaf and defenseless, he had to retreat to the cool of the shade or water to rest his eyes and mind. He was edgy with his wife, his children and business associates. He questioned his friends and berated strangers.

All of the tension feeding this city of millions of immigrants was rising and Naji feared its ultimate climax like an erupting volcano. Sensing trouble, he wanted to suspend the false passport operation for a while, if not permanently, and arranged to meet with his partners to discuss the plan. He knew he would be met with opposition and feared losing the fight.

On the appointed evening, Naji got to the café first. He looked around at the familiar setting where he had been meeting his business associates for years but drew no comfort from the shabby surroundings. Dust covered every surface of every table in the small tea room. When the waiter came by to wipe it off, the dust rose high into the air, stirred like a small tornado, and settled back down. There was an acrid smell and a coarse sandy feel to everything he touched. Only tea, the universal salve, soothed the terminal thirst of the inhabitants of this city and Naji was grateful for its calming effect.

As they gathered in the same alcove where they always sat, unobtrusive and private, Yusuf, the professional forger, who arrived soon after Naji, greeted the other men with a kiss on both cheeks and a hearty greeting.

"Salaam, my friends," Yusuf gestured to the seats arranged around a low table and nodded to the waiter to bring glasses for tea and some dates. He was affable, almost clown-like in his overt gestures and facial expressions. In truth, Yusuf was an impostor — jolly, loud and false — as if Santa Claus harbored a secret that Christmas was a sham and all of the presents were empty boxes. He operated the false passport business just as much to harm the imperialist blood suckers of the West as to make money. With each criminal he sent to Europe or America, he said a special prayer that he, Yusuf, would be personally responsible for upsetting the scales of power.

Naji drank his tea and looked into the faces of the men whose lives intertwined so closely with his. They were his brothers in ethnicity — Muslims maintaining a 21st century façade in a 7th century shroud of beliefs. He gathered his courage.

"We can no longer print the false travel documents," he stated flatly.

Yusuf smiled at the small circle of men who stopped drinking and stared at Naji. They all held the short tea glass with their thumb on the rim of the glass and four fingers supporting its weight on the bottom.

"Once again, our conscience is worried!" Yusuf smiled broadly as he looked deeply into each pair of eyes. He slapped Naji on the back as he leaned in to speak softly.

"Every four months, like clockwork Naji starts to panic that the police will come and raid our little business again and shoot us instead of arrest us, and every time I tell him that is why we pay insurance to five judges and every police sahib in the district!"

Naji looked at him with strained patience. "The Americans are paying them more, and if they aren't doing it now, they will be doing it soon. I hear what they are saying in the consulate. The Americans are watching the Russians in Afghanistan and they use Karachi as a spyglass."

"All the more reason to keep our business alive," Yusuf assured him. "The more unrest in this city, the more people will want to leave!" He laughed with abandon, causing other customers in the tearoom to look over at the small group of men.

"Keep quiet!" implored Muhammad, one of the young men who guarded the small house where the equipment was kept. "I don't even tell my wife what I am doing and she knows better than to ask. But I agree with Yusuf, if we are careful we will be safe. Why should the foreigners care if a few people enter their country to become garbage men and janitors?"

"It is not a few people!" Naji countered, "We have sent hundreds of people out of the country in the years we have been doing this. We have been lucky so far. No one is lucky forever."

They all stared at Naji; he had spoken aloud what they all feared in their hearts. In the silence they heard the ticking of time, not from a clock but from the beating of the heart of the city, insistent and methodical, counting down to remind them of their mortality.

Yusuf stared at Naji accusingly. "And how do you expect to feed all of the members of your household? How do you expect to provide a dowry for your daughters or educate your sons, with your bribery tips? Selling the boxes of pencils you steal from the consulate? Selling cigarettes from your cart?"

They all felt the sting of Yusuf's words. The opportunities for them to make money were few; too many people with too few jobs strained resources and tempers. They weighed the alternatives again as they had done many times before. And as their shoulders slumped in resignation they finally realized their fate and succumbed to it.

Muhammad, disheartened by the truth in Yusuf's words, rose from his seat and walked out of the tea room with the other men from the group following, leaving Naji and Yusuf alone.

Naji stared at the amber liquid in his hand. "This will not last forever, Yusuf. You are my friend, and I will continue to do this but there is something in the air, I can feel it. Karachi is changing, the world is changing."

Disaster is imminent, Naji thought. He felt the historical imperative of change. He believed that his city was leaching chaos and the Pakistani people were sensing it. Foreign influence and money and immigrants of every nationality who were poor and desperate made for a toxic mix. He could not decide if he should surrender to it and join the Islamic fanatics who would attempt to exact justice in the name of Allah or think only of his family. Fate had handed him a choice and his instinct as a provider ruled his emotions. *I cannot abandon my family. I cannot die a martyr's death and leave them to starve.*

❖

The Faithful Arrive

Sahand arrived in Karachi cramped, stiff and hungry from the first truck which took him south to Shiraz onto a camel through the desert and then another truck to the seaport of Bandar e Abbas. Once there, he boarded a small felucca that hugged the shoreline from Bandar Beheshti across the border into Pakistan and eventually to Karachi. Since the port of Karachi is too large to accommodate a small boat, they docked ten miles from the city and he walked. After a week of discomfort and difficult conditions, he was starving and irritable. When he saw a street vendor he ordered *bun kebabs* and *gol gappas*, ate them and quickly ordered more.

Sahand was given the name of a hotel in Karachi, *Noor al Allah*, or Light of God, by his father's contacts in Iran. It was a small, dilapidated house where a family lived and rented out rooms. Stray dogs roamed the streets and the stench and signs of abject poverty were everywhere. Considering he had just spent thousands of dollars bribing people to convey him this far and had no idea how much a passport and visa would cost, Sahand was reluctant to spend money on more comfortable accommodations. His father instructed him not to draw attention to himself or his money, but to look and act poor to avoid getting cheated or robbed or worse. Besides, if all went well, he would not be here long.

After settling in his sparse room, sleeping for long stretches and familiarizing himself with the neighborhood and parts of the city, Sahand was hesitant but resigned to accomplish his mission. He looked tired and unhealthy, not bothering to shave the stubble accumulating on his cheeks and chin. Every day they placed tea in a glass outside his door in the morning and he took it into his room to drink, avoiding the inevitable interaction that he feared would either free him or make him tracelessly disappear. On the fourth morning, after his tea, he forced himself to go downstairs and examine his surroundings. He feared everyone who looked into his face and thought *ferengi,* foreigner.

The first floor of the hotel was one room with a cloth covering the opening to the street. In a corner toward the back facing an alley was an ancient stove and on a table sat a samovar used regularly to make tea. With trepidation, he walked toward the door and saw an old man crouched on his haunches just outside the doorway. Sinewy and rumpled, resembling the ubiquitous urban alley cats overly lean with struggle, the man looked at him through eyes foggy with disease and age. Sahand regarded him closely and wondered if he could be trusted. The thought that this individual was connected to anyone in authority seemed absurd. To be safe, Sahand asked a general question about obtaining official documents and received a blank stare from the older man. He repeated the request. No reply. Sahand started to leave when another man, younger and only slightly less lean, grabbed his hand.

"Paisaa," he uttered and Sahand realized that he would be buying even the most rudimentary forms of information. He gave the man money and was told to follow, at a distance, through the streets until they reached an alley and a house with a white door.

In Iran, schools are required to teach Arabic so that students can translate and read the Qur'an. Farsi and Arabic have a similar alphabet, however, they are as different as French and English. The Urdu spoken in Pakistan combines Persian, Arabic, Turkish, English and Hindi and as a result, Sahand could understand most of what he heard. As they walked through the streets he listened to the children begging for food, money, shoes. They were beautiful children, some as young as four or five, dressed in rags with filthy hair and faces; some with visible sores or afflictions. They looked up at him — running to keep up with his long strides — on legs made spindly and bowed by malnutrition, with broken-toothed smiles, as if they hadn't a care in the world. And as Sahand regarded them from the queasy height of his own predicament, he saw them all like bees desperately trying to survive by feeding off stronger energy sources. Some would flower and some would succumb to the cruel laws of survival, and the world spinning along with benign neglect caused by devotion to higher priorities would have no idea what was lost or gained. The plight of children caught in the crossfire of political and human necessity is an ancient story portrayed vividly in the small villages and large cities of the developing world, with no better example than Karachi. Sahand was unaware of the implications of global childhood poverty but in that twenty-minute walk, the exposed human misery made vivid and real to a boy from a privileged background changed the young refugee. He became aware of a bigger picture, painted and imposed on those who cannot shape their destiny but must yield to it.

His guide indicated to Sahand that he should knock on the white door and then disappeared into the throng. *I will probably be mugged before I get further west than this God forsaken city,* Sahand thought. He looked around to see eyes following him from every corner and doorway. A visitor to the white door was interesting to people in this neighborhood and Sahand had no way of knowing the extent of the network of spies hired to observe the house. The urge to turn back was overwhelming. Each second he hesitated, he felt the heat of penetrating stares boring into his back.

Suddenly, the door opened a crack and a small boy looked up at the stranger with eyes both suspicious and curious. Sahand felt all of the saliva in his mouth dry up. *This cannot be right,* he thought. Just as he turned to run, the little boy beckoned him inside with a silent wave of his hand. He stared for a moment just to make certain he had not misinterpreted the gesture and when once again the wave urged him forward, he moved.

The young boy who answered the door was Naji's son, distrustful of all intruders, but well aware of the reason for this visit. He invited Sahand to enter and in a practiced gesture, took him to the back of the house where a table and two chairs were placed on the dirt in the alley. There was a curtain separating the front room from the alley and after a short time, Sahand heard voices from inside the house.

"Fatima," Naji called to his wife as he entered the front door with another man, "come here and bring your sister, I have someone I want her to meet."

Both men sat in the front room at the table used for meals, work and negotiation. Fatima and her sister, Massima, clothed in the full-length robe or hijab with netting over the eye panel, brought tea and dates and withdrew to a corner of the room.

Sahand could see some of the scene through a slit in the curtain and noticed the women standing like faceless pawns in their black robes. His mother never wore this garment until the Islamic Revolution required it and she only donned it reluctantly now. Reza Shah outlawed them, dismissing head-scarves as remnants of old and ignorant mannerisms that did not apply to the emerging powerful country he was building. Sahand used to tease his mother that she was an Anglophile with her Western dresses and high-heeled shoes. She even read fashion magazines from Rome and Paris. As the oldest of five sisters, she loved to shop and buy presents for her nieces, nephews and sons. Sahand vowed to send her a beautiful scarf or blouse from Paris disguised in a hollowed out book of Muslim teachings so that it would not be confiscated by the censors in the national mail service.

Things were so different six years ago when his older brother went to school in the United States. He had received his student visa with ease and traveled on a Persian passport not yet considered a document of the enemy. Sahand's departure had been dramatic and dangerous and the anxiety in his parents' eyes would haunt him forever. He never wanted to make them worry. He was the son who would make them proud, who would be successful in America and invite them to live in his mansion in California. He was the one who would save them from the horror his country had become.

Naji poured the tea and handed the glass to the man seated next to him. "Welcome to my home," he said. Bowing slightly to the well-dressed gentleman, he gestured to the woman standing next to his wife. "May I present Massima, widow and *saali*, sister of my wife."

The man nodded slowly in silent approval while sipping the scorching liquid.

Naji turned to his sister-in-law. "Massima, this is Ali and he would like to take you as his wife."

Fatima looked at her sister and grabbed her heart, but Massima considered the man and then lowered her gaze. It was her brother-in-law's duty to find her a husband. She could not live in his house forever no matter how close she was to her sister, and she was glad to see the man had most of his teeth and that he was not too old or fat.

Ali stood, examined his potential bride and nodded again.

"I will make the necessary preparations," he said to Naji and left.

Massima knelt in front of her brother-in-law and bowed her head.

"*Bahen-noi*, thank you for providing me with the honor of a husband. I will strive to be worthy of the kindness you bestow upon me." She spoke in the formal dialect of court Persian's called Dari that she was taught in her home in Afghanistan, before both she and Fatima fled the Soviet-Afghan War as orphans.

Massima turned toward her sister and regarded the future from the deep well of her tortured past.

"You and I have feared and fled and landed on firm ground. It is time for me to make a home," she said.

She rose to her feet with that special grace Middle Eastern women have, honed from years of bending in resignation to others' will, bowed again to her brother-in-law, took her sister's hand and left the room.

Sahand was both embarrassed and excited to witness this domestic scene. He sipped the tea brought to him by the little boy who then joined his brothers kicking a knotted towel around the alley's dirt floor. As the tea warmed him, he felt the heat of his humanity returning. After days stripped of all that felt familiar and reassuring, he relaxed slightly only to feel the money belt dig into his stomach like a jagged reminder of his impending mission. When both of the women left the room, Naji joined him.

"Who are you?" Naji asked knowing exactly who Sahand was and why he was there.

"I need a passport, to get to France," Sahand whispered, "Do you know where I can buy one?"

The lines and creases around Naji's eyes deepened into crevices of careworn acquiescence. "How much money do you have?" he asked.

"How much do I need?"

Naji thought of taking advantage of this boy. He regarded Sahand noting that he was tall and sturdy but instantly sensed youth and innocence, and the Pakistani man educated in back alleys and illegal business thought of the many ways he could feed his family with the winnings of this simple transaction. And then the picture of a small boy emigrating from India came to him — a naïve and equally innocent boy following his family's mule-drawn cart over dirt roads to follow their religion and destiny. Naji thought of the sores on his feet, the exhaustion and the thirst he felt during the journey. He had asked Allah to help him never need water again and if he granted this simple request he would be His faithful servant for the rest of his life.

Naji met his wife in Karachi, an immigrant herself from Afghanistan where she and her sister fled when the Russians bombed their village and killed their parents. They were, all of them, the embodiment of the plight of all people traveling from one place to another, forced or voluntary, by foot or engineered vehicle, looking for a place to call home.

"It depends on the degree of authenticity," Naji answered truthfully. "$5,000 American dollars gets you an official looking Pakistani or Afghani passport. Another $2,500 gets you a visa, which you must have and another $2,500 gets the stamp on the visa, which you must also have."

Sahand stared at Naji feeling neither big nor strong. "I don't have that much with me now but I think I can have it sent to me." He spoke slowly trying to think and consider the drain on his family's resources.

Naji considered his young guest and sighed.

"OK, Persian Boy, in five days, be here just before sunrise when it is still dark and we will meet the man who will make your documents. Don't be foolish, you are blessed. How many people have that kind of money? Get on your knees and thank Allah everyday that you can buy your way to freedom in the West."

My father and me, 1987

The Brewing Pot

There is a story my father tells of coming to the U.S. as naïve and starry-eyed as any neophyte immigrant with pre-impressions from movies like *Sun Valley Serenade* and *Some Like It Hot*, dancing to American music played on his Victrola in Iran and emulating the baggie pants and stiff-shouldered suit jackets of Hollywood idols. He tells of arriving in New York and on his first free weekend from boarding school, going to Radio City Music Hall with his uncle and seeing the Rockettes: America personified, singing and dancing in dizzying formations to the music of a resplendent and sonorous orchestra. As he sat in that Art

Deco palace dedicated to excess and entertainment, his head filled with the ripe possibility of high kicking achievement. He was hooked, charmed by the images of unbridled creativity and freedom and like most immigrants coming to this country in the 1940's, he was determined to struggle, plot, and starve to be a part of it. Like those who came before him and those who would follow, he was intoxicated by this emotion of hope and opportunity that erases the scuff marks on the past and creates the pristine sidewalk of the future.

Between the years 1860 and 1920, America experienced its most rapid growth in population through immigration when over twenty million people came to our shores. Immigrants as a percentage of the total population fluctuated between 13% and 15%. When my father boarded his Pan Am jet in Tehran in 1947, he was part of a declining trend and immigrants' share of the U.S. population had dropped to 11.6%. Despite politicians' alarming rhetoric, that trend continues today. Even though there was an uptick after 1970 when the percentage rose rapidly due to large-scale immigration from Latin America and Asia, as of 2009, immigrants comprised 12.5% of the total U.S. population and that number decreases every year.

Life at a boy's prep school in Westchester County, New York in the 1940's was part privilege and part penury. All students, regardless of background or status, were required to have a campus job and my father, along with the American elite and sons of French Counts and South American land barons, took turns busing tables in the dining room. It was a leveling experience and placed everyone — whether scholarship student or privileged pupil

94

— on equal footing. And since you didn't need to speak to clear tables, even the foreign students felt included.

Their accents or clothes or manners — whatever confirmed their foreignness and made them feel estranged and different — were eased when stacking glasses or carrying steaming trays of food to the tables. They were a part of the cleaning or serving team and any team was preferable to the solitude of exclusion.

My father's fondest memories, or at least the ones he remembers as assuaging the homesickness he felt, were of the dining room where they were required to dress in coat and tie for dinner. A faculty member sat at the head of a table of ten boys and served each one with large helpings of comestibles laden with advice. Even now, my father reminisces about the French teacher's wife from Paris who was fond of him and spoke French to make him feel comfortable and remind him of home. As a kindness to the Persian student with limited English skills, she requested that he always be at her table and as a result, meals must have felt like the one time he could lower his guard and bask in the warmth of simple goodwill.

My father stayed in the United States, changed forever by his love of this country and its people and customs, but what of the students who study here and go back? Do they take with them the memories of a positive experience? Do they feel outsider status at home because of their learned American habits? We are educating the world now, allowing more young people than ever before to come here and reap the benefits of the educational meritocracy we have created. India, China and South Korea send the most students to the U.S. and international dollars into our colleges and universities amounted to nearly $14.5 billion in the 2006/2007 academic year.

It is a question of assimilation. In my father's case, he was expected to embrace American traditions and practices. He wanted to appear and act American. We didn't learn any Farsi as children because he wanted us to correct his English, to be an American family.

There has been a reversal. Now, Western cultures are struggling to maintain their identities in a multi-cultural world. Immigrants pour west, become part of a new society and yet maintain their cultural identity. They have no interest in abandoning their religion, dress, diet and instead create pockets of isolated and distinct racial/ethnic pods in formerly homogeneous neighborhoods. The result is often resentment among nationalist populations, the most recent example being the reaction to the increase of Islamic immigrants in the U.S., France, England, Scandinavia and Germany. We are not the melting pot anymore. That clever illustration refers to the 19th and early 20th century immigrants with no relevancy to the current practice of maintaining racial, ancestral, even religious integrity.

We are no longer young, no longer accepting, no longer a refuge for the tired and poor. Our guiding principles have changed and immigration along with it. Since cultural patriotism and strict adherence to religious practices are inherent and encouraged globally, what must we reasonably expect of immigrants? What demands can we make on new arrivals to our country? Will multiculturalism ever work?

Some have declared cultural pluralism dead. They see it as a failed experiment with the result being heightened differentiation rather than integration. In the 1960's the

American dream was defined by social philosophers as tolerating and celebrating the diversity of subgroups in our society. They advocated the absence of conformity and the emphasis of inclusion. But that school of thought has died.

If the fodder for implosion pours over our borders daily, why does America remain intact? Why amidst all of the potential for conflict and disaster doesn't it fly apart at the seams every time one ethnic group comes in contact with another? James Madison, our fourth President, argued that our very differences unite us since no political faction or religious group is able to command sufficient power to separate and thus destroy the nation.

Future conflicts are now shaped not only by economic differences or territorial issues but the consequences of alienation and the overwhelming desire for cultural supremacy. It is no longer a battle of good versus evil; in the last century, differences in political ideology led to armed aggression and resistance, and now, devotion to sectarianism and religious extremism define the causes of international conflict in the 21st century.

❖

Nicole

Every spring in Paris, *Lacoste*, the French clothing manufacturer, had a sale and Nicole Mazeron loved tennis clothes almost as much as she loved the game itself. She bought the shirts with the reptilian emblem for her young nephews, her godchildren of all ages, and for Bob's American daughters. She explained to friendly Californians that the animal was a crocodile, not an alligator, and named for the famed French tennis player, Henri Lacoste who earned the nickname, *Le Crocodile*, for his effective and predatory court coverage.

Nicole met Bob Forood on the clay courts of the Paris Racing Club where French tennis legends and weekend athletes honed their craft in the Bois de Boulogne on the outskirts of the city. She was always attracted to Americans and Bob ironically embodied all she admired and embraced about the generous, confident, fun-loving breed. They were spontaneous and excitable; everything the French were not.

As a member of a strict, gentrified family growing up in the South of France, her life was punctuated with American influences like a cool breeze on a sweltering day. She was twelve when the Americans liberated France during WWII and like some of her countrymen, formed a national bond of gratitude and kinship. There was a small army base in

Nicole's hometown in southwest France where American military personnel took their R and R in the village and handed out candy to the children. She was given chewing gum for the very first time by an American soldier and tasted the sugary sweet confection, savoring every last chew and bubble, forever associating that surprising and delightful sensation with the people and personality of a country she would grow to love.

When she was a teenager, Nicole participated in an exchange program and stayed with an American family for a summer. She landed in a suburb of Cleveland, Ohio, the vast and unfamiliar mid-west. After a few days of awkwardness, she found the family charming, they found her personable and kind, and through détente and interaction, she forged a lifelong friendship. As a temporary immigrant, Nicole experienced both fear and fortitude: traits necessary to belong in a post-WW II civilization populated by the dispersed and weary.

Nicole attended university in France and studied English and Western culture. Why not get to know these people better by studying their language and customs? She started her career at the age of twenty-two by marching over to the American Embassy on the Place de la Concorde, announced that her English was perfect, she loved Americans and would accept whatever position they had available. Since she was tall and attractive with short blond hair, long legs and a body sculpted by exercise and tennis, she was hired on the spot.

Given the task of translating newspaper articles into English for upper level staff, she became the official liaison to French language and culture for the American Embassy. When Henry Kissinger came to town to negotiate the Paris

Peace Talks, Nicole was at his side as tour guide and translator. Late evenings after a day of tense attempts at compromise would often find her and members of the negotiating team with Dr. Kissinger at Le Taillevent, eating his signature dish of *Selle d'agneau de l'Aveyron à la sarriette*.

Each day she arrived at work at 7:00 a.m., finding no fewer than ten newspapers and magazines on her desk ready for assimilation. She started with *Le Monde* and the news and finished with *Paris Match* and the celebrity gossip. The ambassador, nicknamed the 'California Lettuce King' for his large agribusiness (enabling him to make an even larger contribution to President Reagan's campaign), insisted on learning the latest cultural news. Even beyond retirement — whether in North Africa or northern California — Nicole could not start her day before reading at least three newspapers.

Nicole's religion forbade her from marrying a divorced man, so she contented herself with a great job, devoted friends, nieces and nephews and Bob and his daughters, whom she loved like her own. She marveled at how little of their Iranian culture they knew or appreciated and she realized that to be born in America meant to be American with all of its embodied traits, no matter where your parents came from.

When she learned that Bob was Persian, she realized that what she loved about him was not only his appropriated "American-ness" but also his genuine love and admiration of a national personality, a temper of the will that exemplified youth and hope and uncalloused delight in prosperity. While in France, they were forced to share their love of America like a well-guarded secret.

Each Thanksgiving, Nicole would invite bemused Parisians, displaced Americans and any other embassy orphans to dinner and serve a turkey with all of the trimmings. Even though braised Brussels' sprouts or *tarte tatin* may not necessarily find its way onto most American tables, the turkey was authentic and cost approximately a week's salary.

When Nicole was called upon to help Bob's nephew enter France after escaping from Iran, she didn't think twice. To help this family survive and prosper would be a gift she could bestow, with all the elements of human kindness and frailty. She had always wondered how she would repay the Americans for their sacrifice and selflessness in liberating her country and now she knew. It would be like paying dues to an exclusive country club and benefiting from all of its privileges and elite contacts, gaining entry into its shining rooms and manicured lawns reeking of entitlement and exclusion.

❖

The Lower Level

"Will, I need your help. Can we have dinner tonight or at some point this week?"

I knew his schedule was packed and even though he tried to fit me in whenever he could, I ran a poor second to work. There was silence on the phone. He didn't like me to call his office and go through the receptionist, usually giving some excuse that I was calling for HF on Judiciary Committee business. He was sure she saw through that months ago.

"I can't see you tonight, Pari. I've got constituents down from Boston and a huge amount of reading for my committee hearing tomorrow. How about next week?"

I could tell he wasn't really paying attention to our conversation and trying to read briefings or phone messages and talk to me at the same time. I felt like one of those girl Fridays, smart and attentive but blind to the plain truths of poor judgment.

"Yes, next week would be great. Call when you are free." And I hung up.

I knew I had no future with Will but it still stung like the prick of a thorn when he dismissed me. My practical nature forced my ebbing self-confidence to stabilize and instead of wallowing in the futility of this relationship, I decided to define Will and our union as a business affiliation with a common purpose and outcome. *I am using him,* I thought petulantly, *and I will use him until I don't need him anymore.* Besides, at the age of twenty-four, it was easy to convince myself of anything and move on: powers of reflection grow with age and I was still quite young.

A week later, the Judiciary Committee was in full session and about a quarter of the members were sitting in their seats in back of their name plates trying to look interested. Technically, I was monitoring the hearing for attractive press bites but in reality, I was waiting for Will. I wanted him to see me and remember that I was anxious to meet with him.

When he walked in, pin-striped suit hugging his fit frame, no less than two committee staff jumping up to greet him, hair damp from the Members' gym where I assumed he had played squash with one of his colleagues as he always did on Wednesdays, I felt the lateral pull of my emotional gravity drawing me toward him with a small piece of me — a toe or neck muscle — visibly twitching to maintain equanimity, only to collapse like pebbles failing to maintain their angle of repose.

When Will took his seat he scanned the room of testifiers, lobbyists and media and found my eyes. His face revealed nothing but his gaze stayed with mine for the few seconds it took to confirm that I was special to him. Warmth infused me, reddening my face and neck like the outward confession of a willing victim. My mission completed, I went back to my office.

Throughout the day, I tried to stay focused on work. Luckily there was a minor problem in our district involving the Environmental Protection Agency placing an old and defunct battery manufacturing plant on the Superfund List.

This designation meant that the business or original polluters would be held monetarily responsible for the cleanup that the EPA was forced to organize because of the threat of contamination to the ground water supply. We were being contacted by all affected parties, none of whom was particularly happy.

And then five bells rang: a recorded vote on the House Floor. Every office wall clock buzzed and small lights lit up along the lower rim to show how much time was left since the original call at fifteen minutes. Since Senators and Representatives can't just sit in their respective chambers waiting to cast a vote, the official rules of the Congress include a legislative call system consisting of electric lights and bells alerting them to action on the House or Senate floor. In the Capital and all of the Senate and House office buildings, every office wall clock has small lights that light up along the lower rim to show how much time the Member has to get to the House or Senate chamber for a vote. And just in case someone's eyes weren't trained to the clock, they emitted a loud corresponding ring in the halls, or buzz inside the offices, as well. Two lights and two bells meant a recorded vote. I knew the route Will took to the underground trolley from the Rayburn Building to the Capitol and I ran to the elevator to intercept him in the garage, the quickest way to navigate the subbasement level.

Waiting by a large stone pillar in the midst of empty parked cars, silent and expectant, I leaned against the cool cement and closed my eyes for a moment reveling in the quiet and depth.

"Well I guess you never know what you might find lurking in the dark recesses of the garage." He was moving fast — running, actually.

I smiled and reached out to touch him as he passed. He grabbed my hand pulling me with him for a few steps.

"Wait here, I'll be back after the vote," he said and ran off.

I returned to my pillar willing him to hurry, imagining that he would tell me to get into his car and go away with him for the weekend, something we had never done, would never do.

Ten minutes later he emerged from the sliding doors smiling, full of energy, with an ironic tale of the futility of the vote.

"Will, I need your help with something."

"You know I would do anything for you, if it's in my power," he said, visibly sobering.

"I am going to write a letter to Adam Weiss requesting that he green light the entry of a citizen of the Islamic Republic of Iran into this country. As a member of the Immigration Subcommittee, I would like it to come from you. He is going to purchase a passport from the black market in Pakistan," I explained.

His brow furrowed, "Why? We welcome political prisoners all the time. Why doesn't he just apply for political asylum?"

"Because he is seventeen and has been drafted. Iranian officials will never let him leave the country and you know as well as I that one kid trying to get out of serving in the Martyr's Forces is indistinguishable from thousands of others. To prove that the threat to his life is 'individual and imminent', would be difficult even though it's true."

Will took a large breath and expelled it through puffed cheeks.

"Is this a constituent of Ham's? He knows Adam Weiss better than I do. Why doesn't he sign the letter?"

"HF will be writing a letter as well. Two letters, one from the Ranking Minority Member of the Subcommittee and one from a member of the majority party will hopefully corner the esteemed Director." I smiled trying to show my sincerity and appreciation and Will looked skeptical.

"Will, this is my cousin," I admitted. "He's in a desperate situation and we need to help him. Right now he's in the back of a truck or the back of a camel hiding from Iranian authorities and trying to get out of the country!" I searched his face for reaction and the incentive to continue.

"He and his brothers are like my fathers' sons, my dad's only relief from his life filled with daughters, like me!"

Will laughed softly and looked into my face with a hint of compassion.

We were standing close and it was all I could do not to lift my hand to his chest or collar or cheek in supplication. I waited while he struggled with whatever conflicting forces were causing him to reach and stumble over his morals and obligations. He finally spoke after looking into my eyes for a few heated moments.

"OK, but I need to see the letter first. It will seem strange if I just start championing random immigration causes from around the world, so couch this one in terms of the larger picture — subsuming the plight of people at the mercy of their totalitarian governments, real rogue regimes undermining the rights of the individual, or something like that. Then hopefully the Boston Globe won't give me a hard time for bringing more people into this country when unemployment for our current *legal* population is rising in the northeast United States every year."

I must have looked relieved because he half smiled.

"I have to go," he said softly stroking my cheek.

And as he walked toward the elevators I called after him: "You are my hero! I know now and will forever believe that chivalry is not dead because of this brave and selfless gesture, Congressman McLean," my voice trailing off as the doors closed, sending him up and away. *And I love you* — not spoken, never spoken.

Flushed with success, I hurried back to my office and ran into HF coming back from the vote.

"Forood," he bellowed, "where have you been? I need to talk to you."

"Ladies' room," I murmured.

"We allow bathroom breaks? What has this place come to?"

This was his type of humor. With a father, grandfather and great grandfather preceding him in the House of Representatives, it was his prerogative to selfishly refer to the U.S. Congress as *this place.*

He looked down at me from his towering Olympus: "I want an update on the Marathon Battery Superfund site. I will be up in Putnam County this weekend with office hours and I'm sure it will come up."

"No problem, Mr. Fish, I'll write up a memo and get it into your briefcase for the NY Air shuttle." He strode into his office and I, into mine. *And I will craft a letter to the Director of the INS, your colleague and good friend and to the Ambassador to France your old Harvard buddy, asking for their intervention with a small matter currently consuming my every waking thought.*

~

The nice thing about worrying about money is that it is all consuming; you really don't have time to worry about anything else. In 1984 I was twenty-four, single and employed. The only aspect of my future that didn't trouble me was fulfilling my ambition and reaching my potential — high school guidance counselor advice to be sure, but something I felt fully confident about.

Working on the Hill in Washington D.C. put me on the right track but it would be impossible to buy an apartment, a car or the other adornments of adulthood on my present salary. I regretted not going to law school like 50% of my college classmates now making six figures in New York or Boston.

And then my father called and a more significant problem concerned me. A relative of mine, an unassuming man/boy who once tried to interest me in tasting lamb's brains, was in trouble and might even die attempting to get to the U.S. I thought of the great wave of immigrants in the early twentieth century and the people routed through Ellis Island — what they had left, sacrificed, severed, in order to embrace the promise of freedom. I naively felt like part of the noble enablers who readied the pot with ingredient after ingredient added to enrich and enhance the mixture. It was unambiguous purpose I was feeling, maybe for the first time, and I took on this new project allowing it to consume me like an enveloping cloud, inhaling and exhaling the mist of altered eventuality, and distracting me from monetary purgatory.

I studied all aspects of my cousin's plight: possible truck routes from Iran to Pakistan; where he would stay in

Karachi; impediments to his successful purchase of a passport and travel documents; his reception in France and most important, the reaction of the Immigration and Naturalization Service in the United States.

In 1984, the INS was a large and complex organization with four main divisions: Programs, Field Operations, Policy and Planning, and Management. Programs was responsible for handling all the functions of enforcement and examinations, including the arrest, detention and deportation of illegal immigrants, as well as controlling illegal/legal entry into the U.S.

In 2014, immigration is handled by the U.S. Citizenship and Immigration Services (USCIS), part of the Department of Homeland Security. Every day they welcome three thousand new citizens, help American parents adopt 125 foreign-born orphans, and conduct 135,000 security background checks. Immigration is no longer the simple movement from one place to another, it is part of an altered status quo shaped by the legacy of 9/11 and the necessity to safeguard ourselves. Moving immigration to Homeland Security has the effect of identifying every visitor as a potential enemy and every U.S. citizen as a would-be informant. 2014 looks more like Orwell's 1984 than the actual 1984 ever did.

Thirty years ago, immigration was under the auspices of the Department of Justice. That was the good news. Congressman Fish was not only the highest ranking Republican on the House Judiciary Committee, he was also Ranking Minority Member on the Immigration Subcommittee. Whenever we started working on the yearly Justice Department appropriation and therefore the INS budget, the Schedule C's or political appointees from

Justice would magically appear in our office with coffee and conversation, glance at Dante's warning above the door, and proceed to justify their existence. The House of Representatives holds the nation's purse strings and every Executive Branch Agency's spending or appropriations bills start with us in the lofty committee rooms of the House Office Buildings on the south side of the Capitol. Thirty years ago, the INS came to us asking for $539.2 million to fund programs and 10,501 permanent positions; fiscal year 2008 budget for the USCIS, $2.6 billion.

Will, as a member of the majority on the Immigration Subcommittee, was an important part of my plan as well. I thought of this as a multi-headed *hydra* with easy access on the positive side and reprovable influence on the other. It was now paramount that our personal relationship not be discovered or even suspected if I were going to use Will's position to incite the INS to help us.

I knew Adam Weiss, Director of the INS, not only from his reputation as the President's favorite golfing buddy, but because of a series of joint press conferences on the plight of the Amerasian children and their ambiguous immigrant status under current U.S. law. With one American parent, the children should qualify for automatic citizenship at birth, we argued, but since they were born outside of the U.S. most times in unwed unions of local women and U.S. servicemen in the Far East, they were lost in the bureaucratic shuffle. I coined the title *Torn Between Two Cultures* in a speech I wrote for HF based on the Country and Western song, *Torn Between Two Lovers* and found a new respect from the INS press staff. We in the Legislative Branch could be creative and clever after all.

During the committee hearings and press conferences, I had written some pretty decent remarks for both Congressman Fish and Adam Weiss, thereby making a friend of the Director and his staff. I remember all of those conversations ending with, "Well, Pari, if there is anything I can do..." and I thought about their reaction when I asked them to help my cousin from a rogue Islamic Republic with no diplomatic relations to the U.S. enter this country of ours.

In Washington, you can take one of two routes to solve a problem. The first is to navigate the prescribed channels, entering at the bottom level and climbing through the maze of responsibility until you reach the appropriate person at the appropriate desk that can answer your questions, help your constituent or assess your problem — intern grunt work. Once you have uncovered the correct person after two days of phoning and returning messages, you write their phone number in the file with thick red marker surrounded by stars because you have indeed found a helpful soul, someone who knows what they are doing, a rare flower in the field of red tape.

The other route of course, is to skip right to the top and ask your boss, that high ranking official anointed by the public with unlimited power, to call the director of the Agency or Cabinet Secretary directly. Most of the time, this resulted in a similar outcome with the staff you would have found on the phone after two days, getting a nod to handle this case and you taking over from your boss but with much greater speed. After about two months on the job, I was absolutely certain that staff ran the world everywhere, not just in the U.S. Congress.

I decided to call in my favors and write directly to Adam Weiss, a smart lawyer appointed to fill this post from a lucrative private practice in Chicago, who was certainly cognizant of the shocking machinations of illegal immigration. The letter would have to be delicately crafted and personal, using HF's intonations and speech patterns. After all, I was about to admit to the Director of the largest passport policing organization in the world that our poor innocent subject was planning to support the black market and purchase documents from criminals bent on undermining his entire agency.

❖

Revelations of Daria

After I had been working in Washington for a few years but before my cousin decided to hop on a camel and escape from his homeland, I boarded a plane to New York and sat next to a young girl and her mother. When dinner was served, this child of six or seven proceeded to eat and use her utensils with such dexterity that I couldn't help but watch and admire her. When the meal was cleared I told her how impressed I was and she thanked me politely. I looked at her mother to convey my congratulations but she was fast asleep; the compliment emboldened the girl to speak.

"My name is Daria," she said. "What's yours?"

I smiled and told her my name. I must not have seemed friendly enough or her unpracticed art of conversation couldn't find the next entry, so I jumped in with the first thing that popped into my head.

"You are named for a great king."

"A king!" she exclaimed, "not a princess?"

I looked at the mother again — blonde, fair complexion — she probably just liked the sound of the name.

"Yes, a king named Darius, a great ruler of the Persian Empire, a very, very long time ago."

Her young mind tried to grasp the familiar terms and dismiss the foreign ones so that the end product would be a kind of edited comprehension.

"What's an empire?" she asked.

"City, state, country, empire," I said. With the space between my arms getting larger with each classification, her eyes grew bigger and she seemed pleased with her namesake's importance.

"What did he do?"

I remembered what I loved about young minds, free of prejudice, uncluttered by minutia, always looking at the big picture with understanding only simplicity can foster.

"He ruled over millions of people and a vast territory. It takes great skill and management technique to keep all of your subjects happy and he was able to do it."

I could tell she was trying to stay interested despite my pedantic history lesson and I continued.

"King Darius introduced money coins into his empire, along with mailmen and *satrapies* which were towns with mayors."

I didn't want to stress Darius' truculence, rabid imperialism and forced conscription that sent every available male off to war with the Greeks. Western history has a tendency to remember the Greek victories of Thermopylae and Salamis because they were classic cases of David and Goliath conflicts wherein a small group of men defend their homeland against a giant force. In fact, the Persian-led invasions were the largest military undertakings in history and they deserve credit for organizing hundreds of thousands of people and marching them halfway across a continent.

I never learned Persian history in high school. Ancient Civilizations class in my exclusive private school touched on early Egypt, Greece and Rome because of their influence on modern philosophy, science and politics, but the ancient Persians were never given the credit they were due and neither were the Arabs.

And they certainly won't get it now, I thought, *as the world cites the great differences and distinctions between the Middle East and the West and the conflicts escalate and whole populations base opinion on half-truths conveniently disguised in false toleration.*

As I was boarding this plane, I handed my ticket to the agent at the gate. He looked at my name, then my face and back at my name. "You don't look like a terrorist," he said with a smirk. My indignation gave way to a sense of tragedy and foreknowledge of a changed and desperate world. Why did we adopt a national personality of prejudice?

Because they attacked our embassy.

Because people serving in our embassy supposedly protected by a centuries-old principle of international law granting diplomats immunity from arrest and their compounds territorial sovereignty, were taken at gun point, imprisoned and tortured.

Fifty-three U.S. diplomats were held hostage for 444 days from November 4, 1979 to January 20, 1981 after a group of students took over the American embassy in support of Iran's Islamic Revolution. The students were protesting U.S. influence in their country. Specifically, our show of support for the recently deposed Mohammad Reza Shah Pahlavi, who was permitted to enter the U.S. for cancer treatment.

U.S/Iranian diplomatic ties had been strong and friendly from 1941-1979, during the Shah's reign except for a coup d'état in 1953, after which he had been restored to power by the CIA while my father was in graduate school. During this historic interval and interruption of the Pahlavi Dynasty, we had no official relations with Iran and all communication was severed. My father remembers it as the time not only when his country could have started on the road to representative government but also when he feared his monthly allowance would discontinue.

The Shah was guilty of many things including abuse of power, concentration of wealth into his hands and those of his family, and suppression of individual opinion and freedom. He did however, introduce modern conveniences and encourage his citizens to reap all that Western education could teach and improve. If I was expecting to see Bedouins riding camels through downtown Tehran during my visit in 1968, I was sorely disappointed.

Since theocracy was established in 1979, a startling number of educated citizens have fled Iran creating a "brain drain," according to a 2009 International Monetary Fund report. Iran tops the list of countries losing their academic elite, with an annual loss of 150,000 to 180,000 specialists per year, the equivalent to an annual capital loss of $50 million.

Some of the wealth and privilege my family enjoyed was associated with the Pahlavi kings: Reza, the father, and Muhammad Reza the son, who had such great success in bringing western values to Iran. The world recognized and admired the reforms and modernization achieved by the Pahlavis in just fifty years but what they failed to realize was that innovation was accomplished at a great cost. By 1963, with oil revenues increasing exponentially and ties to Western political and economic allies tightening,

Muhammad Reza Shah's power was absolute and his secret police, the SAVAK, were given free rein to eliminate political dissenters. The free dissemination of ideas, criticisms, opposition or freedom of thought and media were suppressed and undermined. Funds, energy and talent were channeled into bringing Iran's middle class up to the standards of the United States or Western Europe instead of creating necessary reforms to agriculture and modern irrigation systems to feed the growing population steeped in poverty.

Business school basics teach us that when the "Haves" and the "Have Nots" live in close proximity, there will be unrest. Simply put, the disenfranchised, without material wealth, will see what they are missing and animosity will build. In October 1971, a celebration commemorating the 2500th anniversary of the founding of the Persian Empire was held at Persepolis, one of the great ruins of ancient Persia. It was billed as the grandest party ever given and tents were erected for foreign dignitaries with gold leaf wallpaper and chandeliers. Two hundred chefs were flown in from Paris to concoct delicacies and one ton of caviar was ordered to spoil the guests. The cost, estimated at close to $100 million, was in sharp contrast to the conditions in the rest of the country where even the provinces of Baluchistan, Sistan and Fars not far from where the celebrations were held, were suffering from drought and famine. As the foreigners drank champagne in an Islamic country that forbids alcohol, most Iranians were not only excluded from the festivities, some were starving.

Could the people of Iran at any point in their checkered history embrace democracy? Did they want to escape from under the solid rock of centuries of tyranny and suppression? The simple answer is yes, and without U.S. and British interference during a coup d'état in 1953, Iran could possibly be a thriving representative government today.

There is disagreement between politicians and historians with that statement. Who can predict what would happen in a country based on altered political actions? Move one piece on a chessboard and affect the entire outlook of the game; move one player in a country's history and affect the stability of a region for decades.

It is universally accepted, however, that Iran may have been on a path to representative government as early as the late 19th century. In 1891, Nasir al-Din Shah, king of the Qajar Dynasty, in order to pay for his sixteen hundred wives, concubines and eunuchs, jewels, travel, hundreds of children and elaborate life style, sold government jobs and natural resources to foreign companies. He unfairly taxed his people and confiscated the property of wealthy merchants at will.

The selfish tyrant sold all mineral prospecting rights, the right to establish banks, and the rights to the only navigable river in Iran, to British consortiums. Russia received the exclusive right to the caviar fisheries. Thus, the control of the nation's most valuable assets were blithely sold, taken from Iranians and given to foreigners. The people began to protest. When the concession for tobacco was sold to the British Imperial Tobacco Company and every smoker (and there were plenty) had to purchase it at a British shop, the people had enough and the Tobacco Rebellion was ignited. An Imam declared the smoking of the British product in defiance of Islam and a countrywide, self-imposed smoking ban resulted.

Fueled by the ability of the people to affect policy, the citizens rose to protest the D'Arcy Concession which granted to the British financier William Knox D'Arcy, the exclusive privilege to obtain, exploit, develop, render suitable for trade, carry away and sell natural gas and petroleum for sixty years. This completed the financial rape of the country enabled by an egotistical ruler who had no idea what he was giving away.

In 1905, fourteen thousand Iranians took refuge inside the British Legation in a city of tents in protest of Muzzaffar al-Din Shah and his policies. The people demanded that a Majlis, or Parliament, be elected to make and enforce laws. A draft document based on Belgium's constitution was written and an elected Majlis held its first session on October 7, 1906.

This nascent nod to free elections unfortunately dissolved because of the conflict that will always pit religion against secularism, and ancient against modern in Islamic countries. In the words of one historian the conflict crystallized "the Persian trait of openness and assimilation against the Islamic trait of insularity and traditionalism," (Kinzer, 2003, p. 100). However, it laid the groundwork for uprisings and protests for the next forty years and in 1947, when the Majlis passed a law forbidding the granting of any more concessions to foreign companies and to re-negotiate the Anglo-Iranian oil contract, history was about to be made.

The young deputy who wrote the law and pushed for passage was himself a Qajar Royal Family descendent and a fervent nationalist and one of Shah Mohammad Reza Pahlavi's greatest detractors. Mohammad Mossadegh, raised in a politically astute family, was elected to the Majlis in 1906. He was too young to serve and instead left Iran to study in Paris at *l'Ecole de Sciences Politiques*, a mecca for young Persians with political aspirations. He received his doctorate of law from a university in Switzerland and returned to Iran just as World War I was breaking out across Europe.

Mossadegh joined the faculty of the Tehran School of Law and Political Science, fast becoming the country's first modern university, and wrote a book stating that Iran could have modern political and legal systems modeled after France and the United States but the country needed to eliminate all human rights violations as well as unfair advantages to the wealthy. He received an offer from his uncle, the Prime Minister, to become Finance Minister but he declined because he did not want to be accused of nepotism.

Mossadegh was again elected to the Majlis in 1924, and became an outspoken and well-respected member of that representative body. He rose to oppose the ascension of Reza Pahlavi to the throne, arguing that he should become Prime Minister instead of King or Shah, but his protests fell on deaf ears. He was a champion of Iran's self-determination but did not have much faith in his fellow countrymen or even elected officials to achieve self-rule. The idealism of his intellect crashed against the reality of Iran's past and practices and he was resigned to champion his causes without much success. He remained in the parliament, discouraged by his colleagues' lack of sovereignty and eventually retreated into academia.

However, in 1951, when the rest of Iran's Majlis finally became fed up with foreign intervention in many aspects of everyday life, Mohammad Mossadegh returned to politics and was elected Prime Minister. He forced Mohammad Reza Shah to sign the law revoking the British Anglo-Iranian Oil Company stranglehold on the country's petroleum resources and established the National Iranian Oil Company to take its place. The Prime Minister's National Front Party, while unmistakably anti-British, was also according to American Ambassador Henry Grady, "the closest thing to a moderate and stable political element in the national parliament," (Kinzer, 2003, p.93).

While the British were fuming, the Americans recognized a justified revolutionary when they saw one. *The New York Times* reported that Middle East specialists considered Mossadegh a liberator like Thomas Jefferson or Thomas Paine. *The Times* reported that not only were the British reaping over three quarters of the profit from all Iranian oil, the native workers were forced to live in squalor and deplorable conditions, receiving miniscule remuneration. Official cables stated that Iranian workers had substandard housing without the simplest amenities like running water and electricity, as opposed to their British overlords in large houses with Western conveniences and green lawns. With these revelations, world opinion swayed toward the ancient country with the budding desire for self-determination.

It didn't do much good. No matter how many warnings Iranians received about a British pullout and abandonment of the oil production process and its devastating effect on the economy, they did not care. Mossadegh was secure in the idea that Iranians would rise to the occasion and not only rescue their natural resources but thrive. However, when oil revenues plunged, the country teetered toward insolvency and its resulting inevitable state of political instability. Americans were convinced that a financial collapse would leave Iran vulnerable to the one thing we considered intolerable: communism.

The Cold War was raging post-World War II and the Middle East was a battleground for achieving world dominance. While the British wanted their considerable investment back, the U.S. wanted an ally, not another Soviet puppet in the region. The Shah, with all of his faults, was anti-communist and that shaped U.S. future actions.

In 1951, Iran was in turmoil; a nationwide strike to protest the Shah's inability to recognize the need for social reforms led to a partial defection of the military. Mossadegh, who had resigned as Prime Minister to force the Shah's hand, was reinstated amidst cries from the people for his return and the World Bank dismissed England's claim that they were entitled to oil revenues in Iran. *Time* magazine chose Mohammad Mossadegh as *Man of the Year*.

In retaliation for nationalizing the oil industry, the British embargoed all oil coming from Abadan, Anglo Iranian Oil headquarters. Iranian oil revenues were $45 million in 1950, half that in 1951 after the embargo and almost zero in 1952. Despite the loss in revenues, Mossadegh was more popular than ever in contrast to the Shah, who was seen as a British puppet. The U.S., delirious with anti-communist fever, succumbed to the British argument that the Soviets were poised and ready to cross the border with force and take over. The situation was heating up and the U.S. and Britain agreed to no less than engineer the overthrow of this popular Prime Minister.

As history shows, through the intervention of the CIA and *Operation Ajax*, it was achieved. Mossadegh went into seclusion, the Shah was returned to full power and a new joint oil company with the west was approved.

All of these years later, we are still feeling the punishment of meddling in Iran's history. In 2000, Secretary of State Madeleine Albright issued an official apology to the people of Iran explaining the intervention as justified for strategic reasons. She attempted to placate Iranian extremists by admitting the ill-conceived intrusion by America into their internal affairs.

Middle East scholars agree that by suppressing the natural patriotism and moderates of all social classes, we allowed extremism in the guise of religious fervor to flourish. The populace, emboldened by Mossadegh, a leader who was speaking to and for them, saw only one thing at his demise — the country that facilitated his downfall — and a culture of anti-Americanism was born.

At this point, Daria took out her coloring book from her small backpack and began filling in pictures of princesses and forests with colorful markers. I now understood her interest in royalty and decided that she was probably bored with our conversation.

"Go on," she said.

"You want to hear more?" I asked.

"Yes, our teacher always reads to us while we color," she replied. I detected a slightly imperious tone attributable to her recently discovered relationship to nobility.

I decided that recounting Herodotus' *Histories* probably wouldn't interest her, not that I could do it after only one semester of Ancient Cultures but I did tell her the story of Rostam and Leili, a precursor to Romeo and Juliet and the character for whom my sister is named. I told her of the *Shahnameh*, the epic poem written by the Persian poet

Ferdowsi in 1000 CE that recounts the history of the country from the beginning of time to the Arab invasion and the introduction of Islam in the 7th century. It is a prolific work, about seven times the length of Homer's *Iliad*, and recounts Iran's golden history through stories of kings and knights and battles, exemplifying the need for a recorded retrospective of the myths and tales so important to every culture's remembrance of past glory.

Then I started to think about the cyclic rise and fall of civilizations and the nature of men. If there is one thing Herodotus teaches us, it's that empires decline, probably because of their inherent expansionist manifesto and that human nature will always invite us to compare ourselves to our neighbors and challenge them in order to affirm our right to claim our destiny.

"My professors would simplify these conflicts as the ancient and eternal struggle of the inevitability of Western individualism triumphing over Eastern authoritarianism. The Greeks believed the Persians to be overstepping the laws of nature on a physical and psychological plane. Every time the Persians tried to bridge a river or sea, disaster ensued. They were tampering with the natural order and lost," I explained to my diminutive student.

This is a western view of this conflict. I couldn't help but wonder how this history lesson is taught in Iran. I remember a British friend telling me that when they study the American Revolution in England, they teach that patriots such as John Adams, George Washington and Paul Revere are terrorists. So, who are the heroes, those that sanctify life or those who revere principle? My internal clash of cultures had once again forced me to question my past loyalties.

I must have become lost in thought because when I looked over, Daria was asleep on her mother's arm, marker tracings all over her fingertips. Looking at her face, I tried to decide if it seemed even mildly changed or enlightened; if I had planted a seed in the world's next great classicist or at the very least opened a mind to the certainty of human frailty and the vacuum of compassion caused by a simple lack of learning. I borrowed one of her markers, and on my small square of napkin damp from a drop of spilled tea, I practiced writing my name in Farsi.

❖

National Parks

Every summer, from 1966-1976, my sisters and I spent two weeks visiting my father. We would fly west, meet him in San Francisco and drive in his green Ford Mustang to explore one of this country's greatest treasures, a National Park. My Persian father insisted that no one visiting America should waste time in the cities. American cities were nothing special compared to those in Europe; however, we had something Europe didn't have and that was endless tracts of land with mountains and lakes and such profound wilderness that the echo of our voices wouldn't reach us for days. The Alps are grand, certainly, and Russia's hinterland is measureless but America's mountains and majestic topography suggest a wildness God created when he was feeling magnanimous.

"This is your legacy," my father would stress, "and these beautiful National Parks set aside for the public's enjoyment and use belong to you."

And with that we would embark on a two-week adventure of swimming, paddling, hiking and sightseeing in the shadow of America's greatest asset.

Even though it was President Ulysses S. Grant who declared Yellowstone the first National Park in 1872, Teddy Roosevelt set aside more land for national parks and nature preserves than all of his predecessors combined — 194 million acres. By 1909, the Roosevelt administration had created an unprecedented forty-two million acres of national forests, fifty-three national wildlife refuges and eighteen areas of "special interest" including the Grand Canyon, and between the ages of eight and fifteen, I saw enough to qualify as a Park Ranger. Most of the time, we focused on the western half of the country and all the glory associated with long, hot drives without air conditioning from one grand monument of trees and rocks to another.

The park hotels and lodges tended to be lofty spaces made of logs and decorated with antler light fixtures and furniture hewn from the aged wood of felled forests. After a day of exercise and fresh air and then dinner, we would sit in the lobbies of these grand edifices and play card games from my father's youth, roughly translated for small American hands and attention spans. My father would muse about pioneers and early settlers and their bravery in the face of countless odds. He never really spoke in specifics because he never studied this aspect of American history and I realize now that the settling of the Old West is romantic to the immigrants, new to our country, who read about it for pleasure. We, who had studied it in an obligatory classroom setting dedicated to chronicling each land acquisition or the tedious memorization of dates when territories were granted statehood, disliked all aspects of the subject.

One night after dinner we were relaxing with tea in the lobby of the Many Glacier Hotel in Glacier National Park in Montana. I made the mistake of telling my father that I wrote a report on Lewis and Clark and he asked me to recite it. The only thing I could remember (prompted by my early feminist sensibilities) was that Sacagawea, the Native American guide, had saved the itinerant explorers countless times from unspeakable horrors, enabling them to safely discover the route across the United States to the Pacific Ocean. My father knit his eyebrows with skepticism and exercised that gift of eternal parental patience suggesting that although that seemed interesting and possible, I must be leaving something out. When he recalled the lessons of Persian history to us, his memory was more precise.

Over tea my father would recount the different dynasties and Shahs of ancient and modern Iran. He had a natural tolerance of royalty whereas like the Father of our country, George Washington, we were wary of the corrupting influence of absolute power. He would talk of his family, as far back as he could remember, conjuring up images of great men in colorful costumes with swords, and women shaping destiny with surreptitious comments in forbidden conversations.

Despite the desired effect of the romantic interpretation of Middle Eastern history on young ears, my father never failed to remark that nothing fueled the imagination like the word *America*. And that everything about this country, from its founding to its economic dominance, had to do with the individuals who sacrificed so much to come here. He was impressed with us and wanted his daughters to know that because we were American, the world was our oyster. He, on the other hand, was forever, if subconsciously, distancing himself from his origins.

Foreigners have a romantic view of the American west because it is relatively recent and stylized. We can point to grizzled men wearing *Levi* jeans with pick axes panning for gold or prairie settlers in one room log cabins to evoke the charm and sentimentality particular to idealizing basic survival.

The eastern U.S., especially the thirteen original colonies, has a different genesis and the descendants of Irish, English, Dutch, Italians, Spanish, Portuguese and Germans left their mark on everything. Put them together and our history unfolds like a scrolled page beginning at the Atlantic with our strong European ties and ending at the Pacific with the fruits of pioneers' bravado.

In this country, all of us look back to our antecedents in other nationalities and cultures. And that is why we are distinct from Europe. There is no one, save Native Americans, who does not come from immigrants at some point and no one who can call this country theirs and theirs alone. We are an amalgamation made strong and diverse by the constant clash of culture, loud and protuberant, violent and condemning, but ultimately sound and sacred. Americans of all nationalities proud of their heritage understand why the ideals and atmosphere of possibility are like a beacon attracting, inviting and cajoling humanity.

❖

The Intern

The reason I love Washington, D.C. and all of its disembodied faults is because I understand it — the people, the monuments, the heat — that make it a magnet for those with a message and a big smile posturing for attention. Elected officials, appointed executives, scholars, economists, bureaucrats, private sector success stories turned public sector problem-solvers, all basking in their fifteen minutes of policy sunshine and glory. They are poised to make their indelible mark on the federal record and move on, citing the gold star of public service on their resumes.

Politicians are a fascinating breed, not necessarily because of their strengths but for the human frailties they overcome with their Herculean attempts to undermine them. A natural politician will overcompensate for the adverse affects of his/her shortcomings. HF was forever trying to live up to his father's ideals, his patrimony and fear of his own inadequacies. I saw this in his overly gruff manner but also in his tired eyes wary of reaction. Will had come to terms with his demons — public school background in a prep school world — and used it to his advantage in representing his constituency, advertising his empathy to the Everyman.

A politician changed by his or her circumstances is better for it. Any life altering lesson, whether adverse or favorable, will lend perspective and tolerance; and tolerance given over to compromise, leading to solutions in all back hallways and public hearing rooms is the stuff of greatness.

There are those not up to the challenge of close public scrutiny, however, and my very first job in Washington gave me a glimpse of the questionable behavior favored by the weak and obtuse. I was chosen among the applicants from my Congressional District in Florida to be the LBJ Congressional Intern for Congressman J. H. Burke of Ft. Lauderdale, Florida.

In 1973, House Resolution 420 created the "LBJ Congressional Intern," in honor of the former Speaker of the House and 36th President and authorized each Representative to hire up to two LBJ interns per year. The intern received a stipend of $750 per month. For the months of June and July of the summer between my sophomore and junior years in college, I experienced Washington as a gainfully employed resident for the first time. House of Representatives offices can accept as many interns as they want as volunteers, however in 1994, a cap was placed on the number of paid staff in a House office and since a paid intern would be considered staff, the LBJ Intern program was scrapped. In the Senate, there is no limit on staff. As a result, we in the House always compared Senate offices to the way you felt after grandma's Thanksgiving dinner: stuffed and full of gas.

I arrived at my new job and noticed a television camera and crew camped outside the imposing double doors made of thick oak and decorated with a metal cutout of the state of Florida. It was the only closed door on the hall. I was immediately impressed that Congressman Burke captivated the press in such a way that they were eager to record any and all of his activities. The reporter grabbed his microphone and jumped in my way.

"Are you a member of Congressman Burke's staff?" he inquired.

"Actually I'm an intern," I told him, "and this is my first day."

Lights off, camera lowered, reporter retreated. The deflation of importance in Washington can be immediate and stunning. The reporter let me pass and went back to reading the newspaper as his partner lowered his camera to relieve the burden to his shoulder.

I opened the door to find no one in the front office. As I peeked into the larger staff room, I saw ten people standing around and sitting on desks listening to a middle-aged woman who I later learned was Lois, the Administrative Assistant. She had strong arms and thick ankles. Her dull brown hair was in a tight bun, and she was wearing what my mother would call a no-nonsense business suit.

"This is a difficult situation," she was telling everyone in a southern staccato with more twang than trill. "We need to do our jobs and keep a low profile. Under federal law, they can't arrest him as a standing member of Congress on his way to the House floor to vote, so he is going to stay over there in the Cloak Room for now to avoid being officially charged, at least until the press gets away from the damn door."

It was then that they noticed me, eyes wide, uncomprehending, struggling with implications of federal law and public scrutiny.

"Who are you and what do you want?" the Administrative Assistant barked.

"I am the new intern," I murmured and immediately thought of Dorothy introducing herself to the Wicked Witch of the West.

"Oh Christ, what the hell else am I going to have to deal with today? Sue, tell her only as much as she needs to know. Everyone else go back to work." She walked towards me, remembering I was a constituent after all, and shook my hand with no smile and no greeting.

Sue turned out to be a recent graduate of Dickinson College and as kind and good-hearted as Lois was feral and rude. She explained in her calm and coherent Pennsylvania Dutch manner that our boss had been arrested for drunk and disorderly conduct over the weekend in the parking lot of a strip bar near the Ft. Lauderdale-Hollywood International Airport, a seedy part of town. Considering I had never met the man, I wondered if this was out of character. Sue explained that no one on the staff really liked him except Lois, who was either a lesbian or his mistress.

At this point, I was tired of trying to act worldly or sophisticated and my mouth dropped open and stayed that way.

"It gets better," Sue said. Looking around to make sure everyone was listening, she continued. "His big political rival and potential opponent in next year's general election is the County Sheriff. So when the call came in on the police scanner that it was Congressman Burke in that parking lot refusing to leave unless one of the strippers came with him, the sheriff called the press and drove down to the club to make the arrest himself with about five squad cars and three television crews."

I wish I were making this up but those familiar with South Florida politics will know that the truth is much spicier than fiction. Plus, Congressman Burke fit the part: florid complexion over rolls of neck skin spilling onto a tight collar and cheap tie. His generous girth was held in check by a belt, invisible to the naked eye, and polyester double knit pants that stretched to the tips of his bright blue, patent leather shiny-buckled loafers. His wife and family, depicted in mundane portraits all over his office, looked like more peas from the same pod.

The greatest job in the world! This man had the greatest job in the world and he was disrespectfully toying with history and timelessness and deliberative power. I had no idea how he had gotten elected but since fate had granted him that one favor in his life, I wondered how he could turn away and refuse to revel in the light of good fortune?

That was when I decided that he did not deserve to be a Congressman, and I vowed to graduate from college and run against him. I spent the next two weeks answering phones and filling orders for American flags because the receptionist, an Evangelical Christian from Virginia named Tabitha, had quit. Being new in the office, I found it important to make myself as indispensable as possible. If I was sick one day I wanted to be missed. By day three, I had the phones and press calls under control; by day seven, I knew everyone's job description and was able to sort all mail. By the two-week mark, I was officially struck with a raging case of Potomac Fever and never wanted to work or be anywhere else in my life.

❖

French Detente

From her window on the rue de Seine, Marie Claude could see the river that flowed through Paris. She stood on her balcony after a long day at the Élysée Palace and contemplated her next move like a grand master considering pawn and king. She had decided not to involve the *directeur* of security but to deal instead with the head of border police at Charles De Gaulle Airport. After all, Bob's young nephew would not be staying in France. It was just a stopover on his way to the United States. Nicole would get him his travel documents at the American Embassy with Bob's daughter's help and he would be on an airplane in short order to seek his destiny; *c'est ça.*

It seemed like everyone these days wanted to go to America. Both of her sons spoke of going to college there or eventually working in New York. In her youth, Paris was considered the only destination for eager, driven students seeking greatness or at least, recognition. *It is the music*, she thought, *or the films that glorify the American way of life. Surely, people must realize it isn't really like that.* It annoyed her to think that children of hers with a heavy link to the glory of French history would rather speak English with their friends than the language of kings. Even the British, *those heathens*, recognized the superiority of French, as it was the official language of royalty and their court for centuries.

And this young Persian boy, following his uncle to the 'Land of Opportunity,' would be entering France with her help and illicit compliance! She was amazed at herself for agreeing to be a part of this folly. Marie Claude shook her head to consider what the world had come to. She went back into her apartment as the rain began to speckle the surface of the Seine and possibly delay the matches at the French Open.

"Madame Lasurrance, you have a phone call," said her maid. She allowed the young Turkish woman to reach the door before picking up the receiver.

"Allô?" she nodded as she was connected to the border police official from the Charles De Gaulle Airport.

"Yes, thank you for getting back to me, it *is* important." Marie Claude tried to picture this upper-level bureaucrat and his reaction to an invitation to the President's office for lunch. His file had shown exemplary service throughout his fourteen years with the *police aux frontiéres,* as well as his recent posting at one of the busiest airports in the world. She was careful not to give away too much on the phone so that if needed, she could administer high degrees of persuasion and damage control in person. He agreed to come to her office the next day and she phoned the chefs at the Palace to dictate the menu: *vichyssoise, sole meunière, asparagus avec sauce hollandaise, pommes de terre, salade verte,* and *fraises des bois.* Checkmate, she thought as she hung up the phone, smiled and decided to take a bath.

Marie Claude arrived at her office impeccably attired as usual and ready to convince anyone of anything. Her confidence level was high after receiving a compliment from Monsieur *le Président* himself about the Chinese state dinner the previous week. She had succeeded in making it elegant but understated. "These people are communists," she explained with authority to her staff. "They do not appreciate extravagance and excess. Indulge their senses without screaming western capitalist supremacy." She had also rejected the idea of having the dinner at Versailles where it was originally planned. Why would the Chinese delegation want to sit in a palace dedicated to royal opulence?

The last time the Americans came to Versailles, a special birthday cake was served to their President and the entire English speaking press became obnoxiously inspired with allusions to Marie Antoinette's famous remark to starving peasants before the French Revolution, "Let them eat cake."

It was a catastrophe and Marie Claude spent a week explaining that, in fact, scholars do not believe the French Queen ever uttered this phrase and that whoever did was referring to brioche, the French bread made with flour, butter and eggs, not cake. At the time of the French Revolution, the law required bakers to sell the more expensive, fancier breads at the same low price as the plain breads if they ran out of the latter. Only the French would think to legislate the price of bread; however, the goal was to prevent bakers from making small amounts of regular bread and then charging more when people had to buy the brioche. "Let them eat brioche" may have meant that the bakery laws should be enforced so the poor could eat the fancy bread at the lower price if there wasn't enough plain bread to go around. *To the victors not only go the spoils*, Marie Claude thought, *but also the interpretation of history.*

Michel Roblon, Director of the border police at Charles De Gaulle Airport, checked his tie in the reflection outside of Marie Claude's office and wondered if Napoleon had looked in this same mirror before entering his wife's boudoir. He had never been to the *Élysée* Palace and was surprised when the phone call came from the Chief of Protocol extending this invitation. When he attained his current position, he always assumed that the invitations would come pouring in, but in reality he had more responsibility, more headaches and less time for his family with a minor pay raise.

"Come in, come in," Marie Claude said.

She was welcoming, with her game face on and well-rehearsed movements like ballroom steps executed with grace and aplomb. Since her hands were always ice-cold, she rubbed them together, lest she stun anyone with their frigidity. As a result she often gave the impression that she was ready to savor a favorite dish and ingest her guest just before shaking their hand.

"Thank you for coming on such short notice," she said, "I have a rather delicate and timely matter to discuss with you and I wanted to do it in person instead of using the telephone. I hope you understand."

"Yes of course," Michel said.

He looked around at the most impressive office he had ever seen, and the woman who reminded him of a slightly older version of Princess Caroline of Monaco. "Any phone call from the Élysée Palace is a pleasure and an honor, I assure you."

He started to sweat, realizing he was out of his depth and tried surreptitiously to wipe his hands on his pants before taking Marie Claude's proffered frozen fingers.

They exchanged pleasantries for exactly five minutes before Marie Claude steered them over to the table exquisitely set with over twelve pieces of silverware and six glasses for two people.

"A young man will be arriving any day now from Pakistan," she explained. "His documentation may not pass your most strenuous inspection; however, we need you to overlook its inadequacies and allow him to enter the country."

Marie Claude picked up her soup spoon and began to eat as if she had just asked the gentleman to pass the salt.

Michel Roblon stopped eating at once. His worst fears were realized and the mild perspiration turned into a stream of moisture emanating from every pore. In his job as policeman of the borders of his country, he saw his obligations as cut and dry. The laws keeping people out of France must be adhered to and the regulations and requirements permitting visitors must be followed exactly as they are written. In his fourteen years with the border police, he never questioned the law dictating his responsibilities and never made exceptions for anyone without the proper documentation.

"Madame Lasurrance," he began, "if the person in question is on the Interpol List of International Criminals, even I cannot stop his arrest. There are international laws and conventions preventing me from doing so!"

"Mon Dieu Monsieur, I am not asking you to break the law! This is not a criminal we are discussing; it is a young boy escaping a sure and imminent death at the hands of his country's enemies."

Michel Roblon visibly relaxed. A political delinquent was certainly less noxious than a notorious drug or arms dealer.

"What are the exact circumstances of the immigrant, if I may be so bold," he queried, while carefully dipping his spoon into the creamiest vichyssoises he had ever eaten.

"A young man of considerable means and importance has been drafted into the army of the Islamic Republic of Iran to fight the Iraqis in the 'War of Holy Defense' as the newspapers call it. He is a Christian," she fabricated, attempting to garner the man's sympathy and embolden his Catholicism. As ninety-eight percent of France was Catholic, she felt this was a wise guess.

"And he is being forced to go to the front lines where he will be burned by the gasses and chemicals they are using to kill the innocent and blameless."

Horrified, Michel Roblon internally admitted that he knew little of this war. He did not read the articles in the French newspapers reporting the atrocities and could only imagine the disfigurement that would occur after chemical weapons were unleashed on the soft human flesh of children. It made him suddenly indignant and he pictured his sons, not yet teenagers, marched from their homes, forced to fight in a conflict they did not understand, given a weapon and promised immortality for killing their faceless counterparts and ancient cousins. He slumped slightly in his chair, physically and psychologically burdened with the hopelessness of protecting the world's youth.

He stared at the painting, *Liberty Leading the People* directly across from Marie Claude's desk. His posture recovered. A woman, part goddess, part revolutionary, bare-breasted and empowered is raising the flag in defiance of the killing and mayhem around her, a testament to ultimate triumph at low odds.

Maybe this young man represented all youth, all untarnished victims of unnecessary violence and it was time for one man to react uncharacteristically, with a voice of reason, he thought. He was being asked to rise above the conventions and petty interpretations of his responsibilities and flaunt a certain disregard for the way it had always been done. His pride and Gaullist sense of honor dictated his reaction to this request and he suddenly felt a sense of purpose growing in his chest, a hint of the inchoate whisperings of the winged victory of triumph.

"How will he arrive here? They will not allow him to board a plane without a valid passport." Michel was already working out the potential problems in his head.

"From what we understand, he has crossed the border into Pakistan after walking through the desert for weeks."

Now Marie Claude lied with gusto and even found she was enjoying herself. The bait was hooked, she could see it in his eyes and she wanted to ensure his total collusion.

"He will purchase a Pakistani passport and visa in Karachi, board a plane for Paris and arrive at Charles de Gaulle Airport. Once he is here, the American Embassy will take over and he will get the proper documents to fly to the U.S. More asparagus?"

Visibly impressed with both the information and the food, Michel Roblon could not help but ask, "Why are the Americans interested in him?"

"Well, he is very important," Marie Claude fabricated again. "And they are concerned that his entry into France be expedited so they can move quickly with the second leg of his journey. I heard something about the CIA's involvement, but I cannot say for certain." She waved her hand in dismissal.

"The CIA!" he exclaimed. The poor man reeled in without a struggle. "No wonder President Mitterrand is involved. Is he related to the Shah's widow Farah Pahlavi? She has special privileges at the airport to use a separate entrance for security purposes," he confided.

Marie Claude realized that she needed to reel slower with caution to avert a disaster.

"The President's involvement must be kept confidential," she stated. "He has no interest in being associated with a covert CIA operation. In fact, this must be treated as any other person entering the country; no attention must be drawn to him. Will you be able to instruct your staff?"

"Yes, I think so, however there is one problem. When we scan the passport, if it does not have a valid imprint, an alarm will alert the agent and he is obligated by law to confiscate the document and arrest the individual. We can clear him at the airport, but we must take his passport."

"He will be allowed to enter this country?" she asked. She served him fresh strawberries, all of equal size and bright red color.

"Yes, we can let him in, but he will have to somehow obtain other documentation to enter the U.S."

"Thankfully, that is not our problem; we will let the Americans worry about that. More wine?"

As she poured the perfectly chilled chardonnay, she felt a sense of accomplishment. *How easy it has been to recruit this mid-level bureaucrat,* she thought. *I have not lost my touch. The President will not be bothered with this problem; I have taken care of it completely and competently. It is fortunate that I am in charge as le personnel de fonctionner tout.*

❖

Georgetown

For some reason, the air was ripe that night. I put the top down on my Triumph Spitfire and drove home slowly, smelling things — flowers, trees, tourists — in a particularly pungent aromatic mix. In Georgetown, when the trees are full and the cobblestone streets glisten with the remnants of a summer rain, the light of gas street lamps reflects off of the water and it feels slightly magical, like a Fairy Godmother is about to arrive in a bubble. I was house-sitting for a Vassar alumna who was away for the summer, fleeing the oppressive heat for the Cape or shore or mountains. Her house was beautiful, not large, but exquisitely decorated, just a bright and happy place to water plants and discourage burglars. I dreamed someday of having one just like it.

Magic though it was, it was still nearly impossible to find a parking spot and I circled blocks for fifteen minutes before I found a space a good distance from the house, where only my tiny sports car could fit. Oh the joys of parking in an American city! How many times had I flouted the rules and tried to get away with it, or been saved by having a vehicle no larger than a bathtub?

I ruminated on the occasion when I had parked my diminutive car in this prestigious neighborhood on

Halloween only to find it the next morning picked up and placed on the sidewalk in front of some unsuspecting homeowner's front door with six or seven parking tickets under the wiper blade. I pleaded with the Department of Motor Vehicles judge that I had obviously been the victim of some fraternity joke at Georgetown University and he decided to keep me hanging through a fifteen minute speech on Congressional staff circumventing D.C. traffic regulations before ultimately "reducing my fine to 0." Then there was the time my much disciplined father came to D.C. and I burst into tears, admitting I had over two hundred dollars in parking tickets and the reason I couldn't pick him up at the airport was because there was a metal boot on the tire of my car.

On this balmy night, I left my top down and made my way past Federal-style town houses majestic and historical. One particularly well-appointed house was hosting a party. French doors opened onto the street inviting the smell of lilacs; well-dressed people were mingling with cocktails in hand, doling out pronouncements and opinions to grace the Washington Post or at least the gossip column in the *Style* section. I stopped to listen to the piano and remembered George Gershwin's lyric, "They're writing songs of love, but not for me." Smiling, I looked to the heavens and said, "Very funny" to the playful Gods of Mischief, always interfering in the love lives of mortals and obviously planting that very song at that very moment just for me. I sang it all the way to my house loud and strong to show them and convince myself that love — requited or not — took a backseat to my present predicament.

My father's phone call informed me that Sahand had arrived, sore but safe in Karachi. He was staying at a cheap hotel and attempting to contact the people who would sell him a passport and visa to France. We decided that it wouldn't be wise to interfere with this leg of the journey as it might complicate matters and jeopardize his entry into the U.S. In other words, we had just so much influence and we needed to use it sparingly.

I ate, showered and noticed threatening clouds from my balcony overlooking the quaint urban garden with a profusion of flowering trees that, for seven months of the year, kept this Vassar homeowner from peering into her neighbor's yard or vice versa. *Time to put my top up,* I thought wearily and threw on shorts and a shirt.

When I got close to my car, I noticed something in the reflection of the windshield on the front seat. I stopped abruptly, thinking it may be some predator crouched or homeless person asleep and vowed never to leave my top down again. As I crept closer, I saw that it was a very large bouquet of flowers propped against the driver's seat: bright pink peonies, large and obscene; magenta colored tulips; fragrant lilacs; all a profusion of color and scent. I walked toward them slowly, fearing their ethereal transience and gathered them in my arms, taking in the moist and fathomless sensory commotion, as tangible as water or silk touching my face.

"I knew you would appreciate those flowers."

Momentarily frozen in place by the one voice I always wanted to hear, I turned to see Congressman Will McLean leaning against the pillar of the house where the party had been.

I turned toward him and tried to regain my composure, even though my heart was beating loud enough to be heard a block away.

"You look like James Bond in that tuxedo," I told him.

He affected a clipped British accent. "Actually, I am undercover tonight, masquerading as a dashing American Congressman."

I smiled indulgently. "How was the party?"

He moved down the stairs toward me.

"Typical, rife with power brokers. I can't remember why I go to these things." He dismissed the affair with his calculated nonchalance.

"Because nothing pleases you more than being quoted in the *Washington Post* or at the very least, being referred to as that debonair, dashing Boston Congressman who bears a striking resemblance to an MI6 operative," I countered.

He smiled at being exposed so accurately and considered me fully. "You look beautiful, just like Miss America with her victory flowers."

"Probably the last title I aspire to," I admitted. "How about a Nobel Prize laureate who has just engineered peace in the Middle East and the eradication of apartheid in South Africa instead? They'd give me flowers for that wouldn't they?" I tried to sound casual with my heart hammering in my chest. He still had the power to elicit an overwhelming physical response from me, despite my desperate attempts to ignore it.

"Flowers *and* a medal, I believe. Any chance I can get the Nobel Prize first? I am after all, ten years older than you." He moved closer to me, making the space between us hot as well as fragrant.

"I believe it is closer to fourteen years but who's counting?"

"Who indeed?" He smiled.

"I missed you tonight," he leaned towards me and whispered. His lips grazed my cheek, his breath smelled of scotch. The trivial banter made way for a heated exchange like the atmospheric shift from light rain to a roaring shower.

"I'm flattered." I tried to sound bright and disinterested, looking away at the shiny bricks reflecting points of light from the street lamps. *I miss you every waking minute,* I thought. *Do something wrong or inconsiderate; make me hate you.*

"You know I can't kiss you here on the street," he said. "Come home with me." His voice was low and husky.

I gazed into his eyes and saw the look that fed my soul.

"I'm house-sitting a couple of blocks away. Come home with *me*."

He reached for my hand and transferred the flowers. I tucked my arm through his.

"*This* is how a Nobel Laureate walks with her escort," I said.

We walked arm in arm along the sidewalk, smiling and lighthearted, as if we had no obligation other than pleasure. I held him close and he kissed my cheek, melting any reservations I harbored on the side of the brain reserved for rational judgment.

I unlocked the front door and led him back to the kitchen to offer a glass of wine or water. He watched me closely, catching my eyes whenever I looked up from my task. He had never been so deliberate, his desire so overtly undisguised.

When I placed the flowers on the table in front of him, he took my hand and kissed the pressure point on my wrist. I closed my eyes to savor the hint of anticipation that suspended time and place, inching toward an embrace of possibility and promise, holding tight to the intoxicating thought that we had all night.

I led him up the narrow staircase cut into the heart of a dwelling lovingly restored to its pre-Civil War splendor by hands caressing and molding the soft pliant wood. I held his hand and guided him to a small bedroom in the back of the house with a view of the garden where you couldn't feel or smell anything but expectation and old pine.

He shed the trappings of his nocturnal obligations — jacket, black tie, shirt — and I wondered if this could ever feel routine or uninvited. When he was done, he noticed I was gazing out the small French doors at the rain. He walked over and enveloped my back and shoulders, wrapping his arms around my waist and kissing the back of my neck. I half-smiled, coaxed from my reverie and allowed his touch to maim my senses and drown the immediacy of truth.

I turned towards him and as the space between our lips receded, my eyes closed and I finally felt my heart go quiet and my limbs go limp.

Never had our love-making been so calm, so mutually beneficial, so perfectly in tune with our desires. We had reached a state of symbiotic precision and each of us met the need of the other before it registered on our conscience. Cups emptied and filled and emptied again only to leave us satiated by the other's intuition.

And as he slept so completely, I felt the impermanence I so often felt after the act of love. *I am free*, I whispered, allowing my shallow breath to escape and vaporize, *yet I tie myself to this man who will never love me, killing my ideals and hopes, for this sense of heaven I feel in his wake.*

The next morning, my car seats were soaked and my radio was ruined.

Part III

And now — behold him kneeling there

By the child's side, in humble prayer,

While the same sunbeam shines upon

The guilty and the guiltless one

And hymns of joy proclaim thro' heaven

The triumph of a Soul Forgiven!

Farewell, ye vanishing flowers that shone

In my fairy wreath so bright an' brief; —

Oh! What are the brightest that e'er have blown

To the lote-tree springing by Alla's throne

Whose flowers have a soul in every leaf.

Joy, joy forever, my task is done —

The Gates are past and Heaven is won!

Paradise and the Peri from *Lalla Rookh* (1817)
by Sir Thomas Moore (1779-1852)

❖

The Black Market

While the evening was still stretched out across the sky, they walked through the half-deserted streets and alleys of Karachi. As Naji moved with a distracted focus, Sahand noticed his lips moving silently in ardent prayer. Sahand had a vague recollection of the first chapter of the Qur'an, known as the Fatiha, a plea for Allah to protect and watch over his people, and he assumed this was what Naji was reciting. There was no real reason for Sahand to feel comforted by any passage from the Qur'an; he had not been raised on it. Like his American uncle he had always dreamed of going to the West and making a life for himself in the "Land of Opportunity" without the burden of eastern religious rituals. He just hadn't realized it would happen so soon and under such adverse circumstances. The Fatiha is also a traditional prayer spoken over a dead body, much like the Catholics' Last Rites, and intoned to either protect the living or bless the dead.

Sometimes Sahand wished he believed in a god. Religion had been a way of life in post-Islamic Revolution Iran — not a subjective part of a weekly routine like in the West, but a command to believe and follow or be harassed and possibly imprisoned. He sadly recalled the time that the

Revolutionary Guard ransacked his summer house when his family was vacationing there, confiscating books and magazines and the board game *Candy Land*, a present from his American cousins, claiming it was Western propaganda, against the laws of Islam. They eventually confiscated the house as well.

He was shocked to witness the appropriation of his peers' thoughts and opinions and their subsequent willingness to accept the anti-Western preaching of the Ayatollah. Boys he knew from school who loved to play basketball "like Magic Johnson" or tennis "like Bjorn Borg" were now condemning all cultures but their own for unspeakable sins against the state-imposed religion. The fervency of their fanaticism was fueling the flame of insurgency throughout the Middle East. He could feel the heat of a million small fires at once threatening his way of life and foretelling a future dictated by intolerance. To abduct the minds and free thoughts of youth is to rob a civilization of its greatest asset.

By the time they reached their destination, a small, unremarkable building on the outskirts of the city, they had been walking for over an hour. The structure was indistinguishable from other dilapidated houses in the neighborhood, save for its shuttered windows blocking all light or unwanted investigation. It was isolated, and if walls could talk they would whisper of desperation and fear through reverberations of chipped paint and pockmarks.

Naji approached the house with caution. He looked around for anything suspicious or abnormal — a car or truck parked too close with new tires or a clean windshield. When he and Sahand reached the door, Naji knocked twice and waited then knocked twice again. The signal alerted his colleagues and they were admitted to a small anteroom with no furniture and scant ambient light. The man who opened the door locked it behind them and stood in front of it with an AK47 assault rifle strapped to his chest. Sahand looked around the dark, closed room, saw no obvious means of escape, and the tingling in his scalp signaled a rush of perspiration to drip down his face and neck. He could not rely on rational argument or impassioned pleas. The people he was dealing with would either make him a passport or kill him and the feeling of entrapment was suffocating.

Yusuf entered from an adjacent door, and he and Naji exchanged greetings. Sahand took in Yusuf's full beard and dark hair and decided this man might be devout; however, like Naji, he wore Western style clothing and sandals.

"Salaam alekum," Naji bowed.

"Wa alekum es salaam," Yusuf returned the salutation.

"This is our 'customer'." Naji stated flatly, noticing the lack of color in Sahand's face. *Smaller men who are less brave come into this room and tremble,* he thought and instantly felt compassion for the seventeen year old towering above him. He placed his hand on Sahand's shoulder and smiled up at him while pointing to Yusuf. "This is the artist who will create a document even the French President will admire!" said Naji.

As the two men laughed, Sahand heard a shuffling from a dark corner. His eyes, finally adjusting to the shadows, caught a glint of metal held by disembodied hands. He froze with the realization that he had no way out if the deal went wrong and it terrified him, forcing his energy to plummet to his shoes. His hands felt clammy and his head felt light. He reeled slightly in the heat of the small room as the smell of sweat and mildew overcame him and he closed his eyes to steady himself.

Yusuf looked up at Sahand and prodded him with his open fist. At first, Sahand had a comical thought to shake his hand but knew that all Middle Eastern cultures did not welcome this Western form of greeting. Instead, he reached into his pocket and placed a bank note for ten thousand American dollars into the outstretched palm.

Time suspended while Naji stepped back and Yusuf examined the check in the naked bulb overhead that lit the gloom with the pull of a previously invisible string. The money had been drawn from the National Bank of Pakistan and before that from the Bank Melli Iran; rial had been translated into dinari and then to dollars. Yusuf's expressionless face did not move from the paper but his eyes found Naji's and the two men stared at each other in silent communication. In a quick gesture, Naji looked over at the guard by the door and nodded.

Now they can kill me, Sahand thought as he waited for the shot from the gun. Seconds passed while he held his breath and closed his eyes. In his momentary reverie, a family photograph came to him of playing with his brothers on the rocky beach at their Caspian Sea summerhouse. He could hear the sound of water and the excited voices of childhood. It lulled him slightly and for a second while his breathing calmed and pulse relaxed he was transported from this sordid scene to a place of calm, filled with carefree joy and innocence.

What was it about this unwelcome adventure that made him remember those enviable days of blissful ignorance? If you had told him ten years ago he would be standing in a room in Karachi, Pakistan with thieves ready to kill him, he would have laughed and thought you were describing a melodramatic movie with no bearing on reality. Yet here he was, barely old enough to be considered a man, and one thread away from death, powerless to save himself, nothing to hope for but mercy, no one to pray to but fate.

Yusuf put the bank note into his shirt pocket while assessing his new client. As he looked up at Sahand, he raised his arms wide apart and high over his shoulders. Sahand braced himself for the blow to his head that would knock him senseless. Suddenly, he felt two hands grasping his upper arms and Yusuf's bearded cheek kissing both sides of his face. Sahand regained his composure and his eyes opened wide to see a smile beatifically beaming from a mouth punctuated by a few well placed, tobacco stained teeth.

"Welcome, Persian Boy!" Yusuf exclaimed. "Welcome to Yusuf's palace of deception and magic. Don't look so sad, soon you will be on your way to freedom and wealth in the West with your new passport!"

Yusuf and Naji led Sahand into the back room of the counterfeit customhouse, which consisted of many tables with machines resembling large typewriters. "IBM Selectrics!" Yusuf boasted. "Naji gets them from the consulates when they are discarded. Each time a box with a new typewriter enters the equipment room, he bribes his contact to get the old machine."

His eyes lit up with unnatural enthusiasm, "Brilliant, as the British say!"

Naji looked visibly uncomfortable at the divulging of his illegal activity to a relative stranger, but he realized that Sahand would be in France soon and out of his sphere of criminal misconduct.

155

Sahand sat down and answered questions about his background. He posed for his 'official' photo and waited as Yusuf painstakingly forged signatures, one after another on his Pakistani passport and visa. He was amazed to see the blank passport covers in various colors and sizes, paper of different weights, cutting boards, printing rollers, ink and stamps and realized they were stealing from more than foreign consulates. Emboldened by the friendlier atmosphere, he asked Yusuf if they broke into the National Passport Agency as well. His query was met with a look of such aggressive animosity that he never opened his mouth again.

When the document was finished, Sahand looked hard at his new identity, trying to find a discrepancy or amateur mistake that would cause alarm and result in his imprisonment in a country with a medieval judicial system. His untrained eye found none and he cast a nervous glance into Yusuf's now smiling face.

"Not to worry Persian boy named for a mountain, no less! I have sent many criminals less worthy than you to the West to escape justice. Praise Allah that you are wealthy, for money rules the world."

❖

Charles de Gaulle

Charles de Gaulle, one of the busiest airports in the world, was having a bad day. Early morning fog in New York had delayed over twenty flights, upsetting the delicate balance of the wheel-and-spoke system of embarkation and connection that controlled all airline schedules.

Every British citizen unable to find a decent meal in the UK is flying here and using my airport! Michel Roblon fumed. *When will they stop talking about it and start building the damned tunnel underneath the Channel to relieve some of this traffic?*

Michel secretly doubted the English and French could ever collaborate on anything and decided the passageway would never be built or that the French would start at one end and the British at the other and the two tunnels would never meet! He had heard one report that the French had rejected the choice of Waterloo Station as the British terminal for the project. The Battle of Waterloo terminated Napoleon's rule as emperor of France. This subtle suggestion of British superiority was unacceptable to the French.

Michel waded through the sea of people rushing to catch a flight in order to reach the calm oasis of his office deep in the bowels of the airport. He saw a phone message on his desk from Marie Claude Lassurance from 7:20 that morning. *My God,* he thought, *those people in the Élysée Palace start work early, or maybe they never go to sleep!*

He remembered with envy her magnificently appointed office and the exquisite meal prepared by palace chefs and then realized that she probably had no life outside of those four interior walls lined with 19th century silk. The note said, "SOI arrives this afternoon at 16:55 on Air France flight #37 from Cairo, original point of embarkation Karachi, Pakistan."

She was direct, no doubt about it, and fastidious, just like her appearance. He wondered what it would be like to make love to such a woman. *Like eating a beautifully prepared meal with no wine,* he mused, *filling but not ultimately satisfying.*

Michel walked over to the border police offices where all of the men and women guarding France's borders were working at their desks, talking on the phones and socializing. He regarded the large staff room with interest and remembered a field trip to New York a few years earlier to meet the Director of Security at JFK airport. They entered the staff room and Michel saw cups and paper plates and brown bags littering every desk. When he inquired what was in these receptacles, his host regarded him incredulously.

"Coffee, breakfast, lunch — whatever they feel like eating," the New Yorker replied and Michel instantly understood why the Americans were anxious and overweight with chronic indigestion. No self respecting Frenchman would consider eating lunch at his desk. Everyone was given an hour and a half to enjoy a three-course meal either at home or at a restaurant. How could they be expected to work effectively on an empty stomach, or worse, on a fast meal struggling to digest as the phone rings and a stream of constant interruptions threatens the ambiance? The thought made him shudder and he reminded himself of the superiority of the French constitution and digestive system. *Let this young brash country rule the world*, he thought, *we will be healthier and live longer!*

He walked over to the head of the International Section on duty until 17:00. Michel regarded him with authority. He believed that he had to exert his dominance physically with outward signs of condescension in order to command respect.

"Pierre, a young man is arriving from Karachi through Cairo on AF flight 37 at 16:55. The CIA has asked us to ignore his false documentation and allow him to enter France so that he may meet with his operatives here."

His nonchalance revealed no impropriety and he stared at this deputy, daring him to react.

Pierre was stunned. "A CIA spy is disembarking here with false papers and they are informing us?"

"Who said anything about a spy?" Michel barked. "Don't let your overactive imagination run away with you! This is not a John Le Carré novel. I am informing you of a delicate situation and asking you to take charge and handle it correctly between you and your team."

"Yes sir, of course sir, I was merely inquiring about the nature…"

"Don't get overly curious either," Michel interrupted. "As the Americans say, only those on a 'need to know basis' are being told about it."

Michel left the agent impressed and fumbling for his radio receiver and his dignity. He walked back to his office chuckling because he had learned the term 'need to know basis' from a John Le Carré novel. He stopped to look at

❖

Cats and Mice

I managed to spill tea all over my desk and papers while reaching for the phone; it was my father.

"Dad, what's happening? We've contacted David Russell at the American Embassy in Paris and he knows about Sahand. Did he board the flight to Paris? Was he able to make it out of Karachi?" I knew I was speaking too fast but I couldn't help it. My father's calm but concerned voice reached across the ocean to me.

"As far as we know, he is on the plane and arrives in Paris this afternoon. Nicole has gone to the airport to meet him with every security badge she possesses just in case there's a problem. Who is David Russell?"

"He's the political attaché at the American Embassy in Paris and when the ambassador got HF's letter, he asked David to handle it. You know staff runs the world, right?"

My father laughed. As the boss of many, he mentally refuted this observation but once again marveled at his youngest daughter's unabashed confidence, an obnoxious American trait in his view.

"Anyway," I continued, "David's a real boy scout but with enough pressure from your friendly neighborhood Member of Congress, I think we convinced him to help us."

There was a pause on the other side of the Atlantic. "What does that mean, 'he's a boy scout'? Is he that young? How could he be working in an embassy overseas?"

I rolled my eyes. "Dad, how long have you been speaking English? It's an expression; it means he does everything by the book, follows all the rules, never questions authority or wavers from the official line of conduct. You know, like those little kids in brown shorts with scarves around their necks and merit badges sewn onto their shirts."

My father laughed. "I am not familiar with that term but if that is the case, we are doomed."

"Nonsense," I placated him. "I work with these guys all the time. The Justice Department is full of them and there's nothing more fun than watching their faces or hearing their voices change when you successfully go over their heads and force their hand."

"Force their hand to do what?" he asked.

"Never mind, you need to get back here, your English is suffering. I'll call David again and tell him that Sahand will be in his office this week to discuss expedited travel arrangements to the U.S. Love to Nicole," and I rang off.

Is he becoming less American or am I forgetting his foreign-ness? When he visited me in college, my friends thought he was like Omar Sharif from Dr. Zhivago — dark, handsome, accented and different; different from their mid-western or New England fathers with balding pates and freckled skin; different in the way he peeled fruit, made tea with ritual and reverence; different in the way he dressed in European cut blazers and Italian loafers. My father was the same size he had been at Columbia; the result of a rigorous and disciplined exercise regime. Aside from some gray hair, he

162

looked remarkably young and fit. I was torn between admiring his distinction and wondering about a life with a 'typical American father' like those of my friends.

When we played tennis in my youth, he had the annoying habit of commenting on every shot I made, whether encouraging or disparaging. We would hit for a short time and then enter into a grudge match that either had me fuming in frustration or beaming in victory.

Once, when he was visiting me at Vassar during my senior year, the weather matched the intensity of the game. The temperature was in the mid-80s, unbearably humid and just like a typical college student, I was grumbling when he asked me to awaken before noon on a weekend. I decided I would serve and hit as hard as I could and hope for the best. At one point when it became apparent that my movement was affected by my mood, he called me to the net.

"Pari, I don't know what's wrong, but you are slower than *a molass* today."

Suppressing a huge smile that bounced me right out of my bad humor, I patiently corrected him once again. "Dad, the expression is 'as slow as molasses in January,' and I'm not sure you can refer to a molecule of molasses; in fact, I don't think it exists in the singular."

Another time, he sent a post card from Paris telling me "the weather has been terrible for weeks, raining cats and mice every day." He was a good sport about being corrected and always noted the mistake like a student learning a living language that changed and morphed as often as the weather. I also believe he took a secret pride in his daughters' ability to know and understand the nuances of American English. It made us insiders.

For me, being a first generation American was like being a mediator between cultures and expectations. On the one hand, I felt the power of inclusion and solipsism, safe in the comfort of my protective singularity; on the other, the weight of history and family tradition forced an inevitable, if unwelcome, imbalance. It was like trying to stand on a raft in an alternately rough and placid sea — one moment of calm to be interrupted out of the blue by a crashing wave from a vague and unrepentant past.

After tennis, we went out to dinner. When a parent visited Vassar the unspoken rule was to bring as many friends as possible off campus to enjoy good food, as the dining room produced prison fodder on a regular basis. Looking at ten of us all dressed up, loud, excited and eating glutinously, my perfectly self-disciplined father with French table etiquette and strict Persian manners reminded himself that Americans love excess — people, food, conversation — and that to cherish their wonders is also to embrace their flaws.

He rarely condemned our American mannerisms but once at a dinner party in France he chastised me for asking someone the nature of their occupation. I am still not sure why, but according to my father, in Western Europe and therefore French-influenced Iran, it is considered rude to inquire about someone's job. In America, it is standard cocktail party chatter. I found myself questioning his judgment, considering it alien or irrelevant.

In 20th century America, I reasoned internally, *we are open and cheerful and conversational. We may talk too much but we can never be accused of making someone feel uninteresting. We are in love with our own story, so naturally we want to hear the stories of others*

— the history and triumphs and trials — because we all struggled to get here and are all proud we made it.

Learning about someone's work helps to define who they are. It's the unmasking of a mystery to get at a person's essence and therefore assess compatibility. We love to question and probe our fellow countrymen if for no other reason than to figure out mutual acquaintances and to feed a constantly curious national appetite for basic information; we are striving for connection. I hear a good deal about the American Dream — how to achieve it, the lengths people go to attain it, the miles people travel to experience it — and yet I've never learned one universal definition. And that is because this ethereal aspiration is different for everyone who can imagine it, everyone who embraces its starry, aesthetic perfection.

Each ancient culture puts its spin on what the ideal human condition is like and places it in different contexts and situations and formations; however it always embodies the same characteristic: freedom — of action, of thought, of religion. America was initially designed to be a place of possibility and promise. And for people escaping whatever fate a rigid class system imposed, it was a fresh start.

Three hundred short years ago, idealistic immigrants flocked to a new life, outwardly unencumbered by Old World prejudice, where reinventing themselves and their families — even histories — was tolerated and maybe even encouraged. Whatever was left behind, whether horrible or honorable, was safely tucked away and left by the river, at the pier, in the hollowed out oak, on the plane.

Los Angeles, CA

In the Los Angeles Field Office of the Immigration and Naturalization Service, Bud Greeley was something of an anomaly. First and of greatest interest, he was a northern California man living in a rival southern California city. He disliked abundant sunshine, the movies, movie stars, anything to do with celebrity, Hollywood and Beverly Hills where most of the actors making seven figures per movie, lived. He disliked Mexican food, palm trees, tropical cocktails and freeways clogged with traffic and smog.

He felt contempt for a pervasive personality that condoned lying about your age and your ancestry. Bud firmly believed that oceans should have rocks, waves and be bitingly cold. He knew that a sky full of bright stars and a full moon was preferable to the neon and wasted electricity of gaudy billboards, and that all the clichés and stereotypes associated with this politically conservative, pollution-ridden city were absolutely true.

On his desk, along with an old 'Jerry Brown for President' button, discarded writing implements and overdue, under-completed reports, was a framed list given to him by his wife Betsy, another transplanted San Franciscan:

You know you are from Northern California when:

◆ You have a bumper sticker on your car stating: "Friends Don't Let Friends Drink Starbucks";

◆ You own 10 pair of flip flops but only wear the one that you have had since college;

◆ You believe the only type of billboard permitted should be hand written, no bigger than a large poster and sitting in front of the organic local fruit stand announcing: "no pesticides were used in the growing of this produce";

◆ You have spent time protesting the proliferation of plastic supermarket bags in landfills, suburban sprawl and deforestation;

◆ You recycle everthing from old tooth brushes to tennis balls because you are afflicted with a severe case of California Garbage Guilt;

◆ You believe that anything and everthing from L.A., including Dodgers memorabilia, Lakers clothing and UCLA and USC banners, should be burned;

◆ You know that Napa and Sonoma Valley wine and cheese are superior to anything the French could produce and that all food from San Francisco, from seafood to chocolate, is sublime;

◆ You feel in your heart that the San Francisco baseball and football teams are superior no matter the stats from their last season; however, you are secretly an Oakland A's and Raiders fan during the Giants and 49ers slumps;

◆ You believe that a ferry ride is the world's best commute;

◆ You know that a good run or bike ride does more to clear your head than a martini;

◆ Your dog is slightly more important than your spouse but on par with your children;

◆ You think the current organic 'farm-to-table' movement was conceived and funded by you with a little help from Alice Waters.

When he wore his San Francisco Giants baseball cap to the office, it always disappeared from his desk, only to reappear in the men's toilet swimming around in the bowl. The same fate was awarded his 'Fog City, USA' t-shirt. *These are the slights you suffer when your family is settled and happy,* Bud thought. His two teenage daughters were forming ties and alliances in their new environment that he and his wife would never fully understand. They seemed slightly alien and tainted by the curse of beautiful weather and beautiful people.

Four short years ago, they were living in Marin County and Bud was taking the Larkspur Ferry to San Francisco every morning to his job as a manager of SFO Securities providing protection for the airport and foreign consulates in the city. He lost his job when the company lost its contract to a Silicon Valley startup that could provide all the security electronically with half the personnel.

Even though he had a general mistrust of the federal government, he applied for a job with the Immigration and Naturalization Service and an offer came back at the L.A.-based field office; on his 40th birthday, he cut his shoulder length hair to meet dress code requirements, and relocated.

He and his wife Betsy, two kindred souls heavily influenced by the hippy counter-culture of the 1960's, decided to think of it as a furlough or sabbatical — a delicate intellectual adjustment which could only make them more tolerant and worldly. Besides, the dental benefits would pay for both girls' braces, and that alone took the edge off the sacrifice.

Bud was born, bred and educated in the 'People's Republic of Northern California.' After graduating from the University of San Francisco, Bud and Betsy traveled through Europe on the back of a motorcycle, soaking in people and terrain and culture, like deprived children ready for their first taste of candy. They both toyed with the idea of joining the Peace Corps but returned home when the money ran out and under pressure from their parents, got married at a seaside wedding on Stinson Beach across the Golden Gate Bridge from San Francisco. Betsy wore her grandmother's antique lace wedding dress cut strategically to mid-thigh with tattered sandals and Bud wore his wet suit. After the ceremony, the entire male element of the wedding party jumped into the waves and surfed while Betsy, her mother and mother-in-law readied a picnic. The one photograph taken by strangers walking along the beach shows a very happy couple oblivious to the responsibilities and entrenchments of adulthood, four parents, ten friends, two Labrador retrievers and a sheltie. The festivities were cut short when the Best Man found a beached injured seal and they transported it to the seal hospital two exits south of Sausalito on Highway 101.

Every day Bud went to his office and dreamed of returning home to San Francisco. Illegal immigration was less of an issue at SFO airport than the infamous Los Angeles International Airport, or LAX, where he was assigned. In his four years, he had seen everything from

169

smuggled jewels, drugs, lizards and rare orchids to a guy who sealed himself in a suitcase and traveled in the baggage compartment all the way from Guatemala.

He was more sympathetic than most and along with his partner, an overweight transplanted Detroit cop whose wife's dream was to monitor any and all movie star sightings, they represented the more liberal agents in the LA Field Office. He took time to explain to people in his high school Spanish or sign language mandarin about their rights and options even though they were basically non-existent, but it made him feel better and it usually calmed the perpetrator slightly so they could be hauled off to detention without a struggle.

Bud turned to his partner and asked him what he wanted out of life.

"What do you mean, like things — houses and boats and cars and stuff?" Alan asked, as he was stuffing an egg and cheese sandwich into his mouth and using the brown paper bag as a napkin.

"No, I mean what do you want to have accomplished when you are all done? What do you want to tell your grandchildren made you the most proud?" Bud clarified.

"Well it sure as hell won't be this job of tracking down illegals and throwing them in detention," Alan replied. "Yesterday, we went over to that FedEx hangar and found what, twenty Mexicans in the cargo hold? So we send them back to their country as two hundred more enter the city illegally every day. It's like sticking your finger in the wall to hold a little leak while water is pouring over the top of the dam. It's nothing I'm *proud* of but it pays the bills and my wife loves the weather. Besides, none of the politicians will say it because it makes them sound bad or unsympathetic or something, but the immigrant population is filling a piece of the employment pie that people born here are not necessarily interested in filling, if you get my drift."

A fellow agent ambled over and joined the conversation.

"That's true and we all know it. When's the last time you saw an 'American' guy mowing a lawn? Or busing tables in a restaurant? Or plucking chickens at the plant or stacking boxes at the warehouse? We sit here and patrol the borders, or monitor the airport in our case, against these illegals when most of them are here to work, make money, and send it back home to bring more of their family here."

Alan nodded. "They can't apply for welfare or food stamps because they're off the grid. Sometimes I wonder why we work so hard to keep people out. Why not just extradite the criminal element and leave the others alone?"

"Hey, you know what I read in the paper the other day?" Another agent joined the conversation. "More than 40% of current Fortune 500 companies were founded by an immigrant or a child of an immigrant. And guess what, paesanos? That would be me."

There was a silence in the large space populated by ordinary people at ordinary desks with fluorescent lights humming like droning bees as they all considered their ancestry, their families, their mission and the laws they were sworn to protect.

Bud looked at his colleagues and heaved a sigh. *We are an experiment,* he thought. *We are young and brash and daring but we are untested and inexperienced and maybe, just maybe, we are getting this one wrong. The U.S. is never going to be like France or England or Germany with their homogeneous population base. We will always be the country of people from somewhere else.*

And then he wondered about the logistics of this job he did every day. He interviewed people, listened to them, looked into their faces and tried to determine if they were confessing or lying out of fear. He very much wanted to do the right thing, give people a chance, correct a mistake, help start a life. He had always played the referee or the guy who looked at the bigger picture and illuminated the counter perspective to the feuding parties. He was a fixer by nature, a placater of problems and yet in this arena, he could only grant temporary appeasement. Both sides were rarely happy at the outcome and he was left in the middle, stifled between the streaming raging horde and the rapidly closing door.

Last week he walked into a mosque to question its leader and assess the possibility of its use as a way station where people who entered the U.S. from Canada connected to housing and jobs and melted into the daily traffic of southern Californian life. While he waited to question the Imam, he watched as men bowed and prayed with rapt attention and respect.

As he regarded a scene that could have been in the Middle East, he marveled at how this city, any American city or town, grew to accommodate its latest arrivals. There were problems, certainly, and unrest and violent clashes but there were also Korean markets and Russian Restaurants and Little Tehran right in the middle of Los Angeles. He thought of Betsy's work at the local elementary school helping parents and children assimilate into their new country and register for ESL or 'English as a Second Language' classes. Most people assume that all of the students are Latino learning English and yet minimally,

172

eight nationalities and languages are represented in each grade.

After he learned nothing from the enigmatic but polite Imam, he scanned the surroundings for unusual activity and noticed a man walking from the mosque toward the parking lot and decided to approach him. Bud always tried to extract information in the friendliest way possible. People with something to hide often times found him less threatening; his attitude, demeanor and posture evoked calm and fairness, traits not usually associated with law enforcement. He waved at the man and greeted him, introducing himself as a new member of the neighborhood.

"Are all of the worshippers inside this mosque Muslims from a certain country?" Bud tried to sound like a casually interested citizen.

The man was elderly, small and compact with dark friendly eyes, a short white beard and a bald scalp with white thinning hair around the edges. He looked at Bud with a tired but patient expression.

"Most are from Iran," the man explained carefully. "We are here in Los Angeles as refugees. Some of us have fled from the revolution that threatened to take everything we owned and place us in jail." He stopped speaking to assess Bud's level of interest and reaction. The gentleman reached out his hand to steady himself on Bud's arm as they walked.

"We had nowhere to go so some Persians are in France, some in other parts of the U.S. and Canada but many have come to this city." He stopped walking and straightened slightly, putting his hand on his chest with pride. "We are the second largest minority population in Los Angeles County after the Spanish-speaking people, of course." He was soft-spoken with a pleasant accent and Bud wondered

173

how anyone could justify incarcerating this man who exuded calm.

"Your English is great," Bud remarked. "How long have you been here?"

The man's face broadened and stretched with the compliment. "I taught literature at the University of Tehran where most of the professors spoke English and French. When the Islamic Revolution began and the Shah was overthrown, the Ayatollah's representatives expelled or arrested anyone who seemed suspicious. Many at the University were fired for not strictly adhering to the imposed teaching guidelines, but we are the lucky ones. Most are still there, unable to emigrate. Not everyone is accepted into this country, you know. For every person here there are hundreds whose applications are rejected." The older gentleman had no idea that his comments were well known to his listener.

"In many cases our property and personal possessions were confiscated. When we left, we took nothing with us but the clothes on our backs. But I still feel blessed — to be alive, to be healthy and to be free. I consider Los Angeles my home now."

Bud watched this humble man in his socks and slippers as he made his way slowly down the street. What would it mean to be displaced, a person without a home, a man without a country? It made his eyes tired and his throat dry and he rubbed his face hard to try and erase the image. *We took nothing with us but the clothes on our backs.*

Bud walked to his car disillusioned by his original task, trying to feel comfort from the firm ground beneath him and the typical landscape of American suburbia. He sensed

174

the impermanence of a world that could grant you privilege one day and take it away the next and it frightened him.

As he sat in his car looking around at the quiet neighborhood he realized that since our founding, Americans have never known violent regime change. *We have always been here like a life raft between two oceans to offer safety from the tossing tides of the world's changing ideological and religious storms. Our founding is based on the acceptance of displaced and alienated groups. How can we turn people away?*

And yet, it was his job to do so every day.

❖

The Trap

Sahand officially entered the sanctified country of France and smiled for the first time in a month. He waited in the line designated for foreign passengers with businessmen and tourists from the Middle East. Wealthy men in suits with briefcases, some in djellabahs, and women with Chanel shoes peeking out from under their burqas, coming to Paris to buy couture and wear it hidden under robes in the oil-soaked Gulf States.

As the line moved slowly but methodically toward the glass cubicles manned by French gendarmes, a sense of peace descended onto Sahand from a place he did not know existed. All of the uncertainties lifted like steam off freshly brewed tea and he breathed in the air of a stable and orderly country. With freedom in front and fear behind, he allowed himself to dream of his life in America. He wanted to study biochemistry at a university and banter with the professor in an open atmosphere that welcomed the friendly jousting of ideas and opinions, to eat ice cream at a café with a girl in shorts and to wear a t-shirt with a large swoosh on it and the words, "Just Do It." He wanted to laugh out loud at the radio or television when it made fun of the President or the Congress or the Supreme Court and become familiar with the democratic system so that he could one day be a living, breathing part of it. He wanted to go to the movies and see *Star Wars.*

The flight crew walked by their former charges wheeling their bags and chatting amiably, glad to be home. As they made their way to their special line, one of the stewardesses bumped into Sahand and looked up into his face.

"Pardonnez moi," she said. For a brief moment they shared eye contact and Sahand allowed his heart to flutter and trip over the prospect of parallel encounters with pretty girls.

His daydream lasted until the official waved him forward and he stepped across the blue line to present his documents. The intoxication of pleasant thoughts evaporated his fear like bubbles in champagne and he forgot to be nervous, forgot that his passport was false, created by criminals in a small house on the fringe of Karachi, and forgot that he wasn't like everyone else standing around him. He stepped up to the desk and smiled at the uniformed immigration agent as he handed over his documents. The man looked at Sahand with the unrestrained boredom of a drone stuck in a mid-level job with a repetitive task.

He scanned the Pakistani passport into the computer and immediately an alarm pierced the air. Within seconds, two uniformed men were standing on either side of Sahand and the immigration agent was barking at him in French.

"Where did you get this?" the official shouted, holding the passport in Sahand's face with his photo staring back at him like an accusation.

As the lights of the room began to get brighter and the atmosphere more charged and heated, Sahand could not remember how to speak French and became mute. People were staring at him and pointing. A million different languages could be heard questioning, accusing and exclaiming. Suddenly the scene had changed and he was in a completely different place from where he had been moments before.

When he had called from Cairo, his uncle had assured him that the officials knew he was coming. What went wrong? His eyes scanned the room for the exit signs with freedom and anonymity on the other side. If he ran through the doors would they chase him? When should he attempt it? Now, or when they were putting him on the plane to go back to Iran? His hands twitched as they were not restrained. The men on either side of him were not holding him...yet.

Sahand quickly considered one of the uniformed guards at his side. He was well-groomed and healthy looking but small, no larger than six feet tall. *I can outrun him,* he thought. He devised a plan quickly in his head. He would push the one on his right and run through the door marked exit, creating havoc and confusion while heading for the street. Once outside there were a million places to hide. This was civilization. They would not shoot him in the street. His feet itched with the prospect of an imminent take off.

His breath became short in anticipation; his eyes darted from one official to another to assess their physical acuity and stamina. The police seemed to regard him with suspicion and hostility, ready to act at the slightest provocation.

As the agent began opening his visa a loud bell rang and he picked up the phone in his booth and held it to his ear as he stared at Sahand.

"Oui," seconds passed, "oui," and then he hung up. Slowly he placed the Pakistani passport and visa so carefully counterfeited and inspected, so expensive and valuable, in a drawer in front of him, looked at both guards flanking Sahand and at the petrified young man. His expressionless eyes stared into Sahand's face for what seemed like hours.

"You are free to go monsieur," he said, and waved the next person to his station. The two guards at his sides ambled away to their posts and Sahand, wet with sweat, breathless with the prospect of failure, walked with the weight of the world like a steel ball on his shoulders, to baggage claim.

❖

America Abroad

David Russell began each day with a run through the
Jardin des Tuileries, one of the most beautiful urban parks
in the world. This was the best part of working in Paris —
the buildings and wide streets and open plan of the city
with myriad parks and historic buildings, all pleasing to the
eye and the runner. The layout of Paris was designed and
executed by Pierre L'Enfant who subsequently planned the
placement of the streets and monuments of Washington
D.C. The city's grid made perfect sense to David who had
majored in political science at Stanford but minored in
mathematics. Cities should be geometric, radiating energy
and beauty from the center outward like concentric circles,
one after another, in faultless proportioned succession.

David was teased for his love of order but when he
scored a near perfect mark on the Foreign Service Exam
and was offered any posting in Western Europe or Japan,
his classmates were impressed. He chose Paris because he
had a decent command of the French language and felt he
understood the culture better than others. The French were
not frivolous like the Italians, they were not filled with self-
importance like the British nor suffering from an inferiority
complex like the Germans.

His five-foot, eight-inch frame was in perfect proportion
because of consistent exercise and his fair hair and small

features reminded people of the boy he once was as opposed to the man he would someday be. After showering and shaving, he usually arrived at his office by 8 a.m., read the press transcriptions by Nicole Mazeron and checked the Ambassador's schedule. It was his job to make sure the Ambassador was prepared for all meetings with the correct briefings and background papers. *The man would not be able to perform his job competently without me,* David thought.

As he entered his office, Jean Marie, who insisted on being called an Assistant and not a Secretary, reminded him that the office of Congressman Hamilton Fish, Jr. of New York was expecting him to meet with a young man about receiving an expedited student visa. *Probably another academically substandard French kid trying to get into Brown,* David mused. He picked up the phone to return the call from Fish's Press Secretary in D.C.

At that precise moment, Sahand entered the American Embassy with Nicole as escort. He noticed the American marines guarding the entrance and the French police surrounding the building and couldn't decide if he felt safe or threatened in this fortress shadowed by an ancient Egyptian obelisk on the Place Vendome.

Nicole's phone rang. David Russell was making a valiant attempt at small talk: Yes, she knew Congressman Fish's Press Secretary. Yes, it was a small world and Washington wasn't half as interesting as Paris or as livable as New York. Yes, she would consider adding political cartoons to the morning press translations. Nicole hung up and sent the recently arrived visa applicant to the fourth floor to meet the man who would either make his entry into the U.S. a reality or a pipe dream.

Sahand rode the carpeted lift in stony isolation. He was unsure how to act in this interview — confident, humble, or clueless. He decided he would try to think and walk like an American so that David Russell wouldn't have to stretch his imagination too far to make it official. The ornate elevator opened onto a hallway that unmasked the building's original purpose as the private home of lesser royalty. High ceilings and scrollwork, columns and balustrades decorated the walls and Sahand was reminded of photographs of grand houses and palaces that portrayed people like small fish in a vast ocean. Portraits of President Reagan and Vice President George H.W. Bush hung strategically alongside an early landscape of the U.S. Capitol Building circa 1820, and he couldn't help but wonder if being handsome or photogenic was a prerequisite for office in America. Thick red carpet lined the hallway muting all office conversation causing his thoughts to reverberate with intensity.

At each footfall Sahand felt the hushed and weighty succession of all candidates for admission to the West or American aid, treading down the hallowed halls gilded by French tradition and stamped with America's unshakeable influence. They were walking with him, shoulder to shoulder, afraid but determined, emboldened by the eternal instinct to find a home.

America has always had a schizophrenic relationship with Europe. We are, relatively speaking, the new kid on the block and Europeans condescendingly indulge us like an errant child, strong and athletic, scruffy and bruised but inherently kindhearted and one-dimensional. We are made of their detritus, the radical ideas and theories rejected by old regimes but used to pave the way for a changing order in the testing ground of the bold New World. Our nascent steps, our growth, our dominance allow us the temporary victory and the fleeting pleasure to savor the unintended ironies of our survival.

We are feared, respected, and resented. We have looked to Europe for help and they have reciprocated. Enemies in war became compliant in peace and then superior in a world economy where Adam Smith, capitalism and profit are god. In a fast-changing world, success, solvency and superiority are as ephemeral as celebrity. In a global culture that demands and reveres the qualities of youth, America was the coveted champion.

Sahand entered the office at the end of the hall and was shown into an inner room. When the two men shook hands he realized that he towered over David Russell but tried to appear less intimidating by stooping his shoulders and hanging his head. The effect was unfortunate and reminded the diminutive American official of a large shaggy dog, friendly but overpowering.

"Why do you want to go to the U.S.?" David asked indicating a seat in front of his desk for Sahand to use.

"I want to study at a University in America and engage in the free exchange of ideas." He had been practicing this response for weeks and it sounded as canned as it felt.

David Russell was preoccupied by the search for his reading glasses and Sahand took the silence to mean he should continue.

"I tried hot dogs and ketchup as a child with my American cousins and since I liked them very much, I decided that I wanted to come to America!" He blurted out, thinking he was making an amusing joke and waiting for the bureaucrat to smile.

David looked up from his desk. "Mustard," he corrected.

"Excuse me?" Sahand asked.

"Hot dogs and mustard," David reiterated. "Hamburgers and ketchup or even French fries, but hot dogs go with mustard."

Not being well versed in the intricacies of condiment use, Sahand had no idea what he was talking about so he nodded sagely and tried to say mustard like someone who knew its proper use.

"Let me get this straight," David Russell always embraced the salient facts without pretense. "You are basically a political refugee; however, because you left under extenuating circumstances you were unable to locate your passport or apply for a visa. Is that correct? And you traveled under duress from Iran to Pakistan and obtained travel documents in Karachi?"

Sahand wasn't sure of the meaning of 'extenuating' but he did not have a passport or visa so he answered in the affirmative.

"Where are your current passport and visa?"

This he understood. "The French took them at the airport."

"Ah, I see, well we cannot begin the process of issuance of a U.S. student visa without a valid passport. A visa has to accompany an official document verifying the citizen's status and nationality, you see, it cannot stand alone. Will you be using your Persian passport?"

Sahand didn't have a Persian passport and simply shook his head.

"Ah, I see, well what legal document will you be using to accompany your f-1 student visa?" David Russell took a deep breath and thought of inventing a tutorial that the State Department could circulate to all embassies for all foreign students describing the process and necessities for studying in the United States.

"I don't know," Sahand replied slightly bewildered and afraid. He had assumed this man would be able to give him all necessary documents for his entry into the U.S. and not ask stupefying questions.

"I see," David Russell said for the third time. He realized that this was going to be more complicated than he originally anticipated and quite different from the chore that nice Congressional Aide described. New York Congressman or not, this fellow could not travel on his good looks and connections alone.

"You need a passport," he stated flatly but not without kindness. Sahand stared at him dumbstruck and confounded, unable to offer an alternative solution.

The Political Attaché put the f-1 student visa application aside using his body language to dismiss the young man sitting across from him. Sahand did not move; he was not being rude or stubborn he was just unaware of the subtlety of bureaucratic dismissal.

David Russell stood and offered his hand in his most magnanimous, practiced manner and Sahand stood to shake it, wondering what had just transpired. When he reached the door, he turned back and smiled at the gentleman as he was told that Americans either smiled or laughed all the time and he wanted so desperately to be like them, to be one of them.

❖

Baiting the Hook

"Here's the letter." I handed Will my draft to Adam Weiss, Director of the INS. "I just need a piece of your stationery."

It was 9:30 p.m. and he had let everyone in his office go home even though the House of Representatives was still in session. He had piles of papers on his desk and some stacked on the floor. Staff-written memoranda were also taped to the back of his chair. We tried this with HF but he just ignored them and it looked like Will did too. There was so much material to assimilate that the amount of briefings and staff memos not to mention committee reports was often times overwhelming. To expect each Member of Congress to be an expert on everything they vote on is, quite frankly, unrealistic.

The best that Representatives can do is understand the issue on the House floor. They must, though, have a degree of expertise for anything at the committee level. Party caucuses worked hard to publicize and promote each party line and we were often advised to support or reject a piece of legislation. HF followed their recommendations about half of the time but Will, in the majority, was a loyal Massachusetts Democrat and did whatever House Speaker Tip O'Neill told him to. Sometimes I teased Will that the

186

stout Speaker threatened to sit on anyone who disagreed with him.

Will was absorbed in his work. He saw these late night sessions as opportunity to catch up on paperwork and liked the quiet when halls didn't echo with the rapid footfalls of mass visitation.

He had a great view of the Capitol from his office and I laughed inwardly at the trappings and perks of the majority. HF had more seniority than Will but because we were in the minority, we made due with smaller quarters and a less impressive view. I gazed out of the big window in Will's office and noticed that the dome perched on top of the Capitol was glowing, lit by a torch to signify one or both Houses of Congress in session. The Statue of Lady Liberty inside the dome, illuminated and resplendent, confers peace, prosperity and justice on all the inhabitants of this purposeful body. In one hand she holds a sword and the other, a laurel wreath of victory and the shield of the United States, a salute to our belligerent past and hopes for our triumphant future.

Will was considering the letter, making changes and I was standing behind him reading the messages on the back of his chair. I reached over the top and began massaging his shoulders. At once relaxed, he leaned back and the furrowed brow of concentration gave way to a boyish smile perched under translucent hazel eyes. I came around and half sat on his desk, my black watch kilt resting on a letter from the President.

He pulled at the pin that held both sides of the skirt together. "If I unfasten this pin, will your skirt fall apart?" he teased.

"Will, keep reading! I want to get this letter out tomorrow!" I implored. "My cousin is already in Paris which means that he may be flying to the U.S. as early as next week and Adam Weiss may take a week to read his mail! I don't want INS agents jumping him the minute he lands in California."

Will was still fingering my kilt pin and reading simultaneously when he looked up, leapt from his desk and walked into the staff room. He came back with some stationery and envelopes and handed them to me.

"Thanks," I said, "I think I'll get this out tonight by courier and then send HF's letter tomorrow the same way."

I touched his bare arm where the rolled sleeve revealed a taut muscled tendon.

"Squash is making you fit or is this from working out in the gym?" I asked.

"Carrying twenty pounds of papers around is giving me tendonitis!" he complained. "I'm glad it's at least as attractive as it is painful. Actually I think I'm working too hard. I forgot to read the job description before I ran for Congress." His smirk belied a half-truth.

Since 1789, approximately 12,000 men and women have had the distinction of serving as Members of Congress and none was furnished with a job description before taking office. Article I of the U.S. Constitution sets forth the composition and powers of the Congress and the qualifications necessary for election. However, there is no discussion of specific duties for Members of the House or Senate.

This has two uneasy outcomes: first, unqualified people run for Congress. With only a cursory knowledge of the machinations of the federal government in general and the legislative branch in particular, lawyers, accountants, small business owners and community activists arrive with plans and ideas that are often times untenable. Once they arrive in Washington, they get lost in mastering the process and defer to their party leadership on everything. Free thinking, idealistic, anti-Washington freshmen Congressmen and women hit the ground running and slam into the force field known as 'Practices and Procedures of the House of Representatives' (or Senate). And the second outcome is that some individuals face a harsh realization when they arrive to fulfill their duty and take their place as policy shapers in the most important deliberative body in the Free World: they are in over their heads and unable to do anything but concur or object. Burnout is fast and turnover is imminent.

According to the Center on Congress, a member of Congress has ten basic duties: local representation, constituency service, national policy making, committee work, oversight and investigation, floor work, congressional leadership, political leadership, educating, office management and in the Senate, advise and consent of Presidential appointments.

It's difficult to prioritize these responsibilities. On any given day, an important floor vote may take precedence over a vital constituent meeting or a congressional delegation caucus. Members have to make a snap judgment of where to put their energy and hope it's the right place. They rely heavily on briefings, memos condensing issues into sound bites and the ever-present staff.

It's no wonder Congressmen receive mediocre approval ratings, trying to educate, inform and appease 500,000 people while exerting leadership over colleagues and party regulars nationally and deciding the course of the nation from federal funding for local libraries to foreign aid.

No one is really sympathetic to this plight and even a grandmother doesn't feel sorry for an elected official but for all of the hours and the amount of vexing assimilation, they deserve some credit. We all did. As a twenty-four year old Press Secretary trading job horror stories with my private sector peers, I quickly learned that I worked harder than any of my friends. It was like coming home that first Christmas break from college and learning that all of the kids who were at Ivy League schools had half the homework and a much lighter required class schedule than I. Banker's hours were no joke and I thought about the times I came in on a Saturday to finish a newsletter to our constituency because HF insisted that it go out on Monday.

Once, I dragged myself in on a weekend only to find Congressman Fish in his office engaged and preoccupied. I went to my desk and worked for a while until I heard the familiar bellow, "Forood!"

"You rang?" I quipped.

He smiled. "I want you to help me with something, a letter I want to write." He seemed to be struggling with how to compose it. "It's a serious letter to a high ranking official and I don't want it to be taken lightly."

I felt like reminding him that I was the one who put, "Give my regards to Broadway" in the closure to New York City Mayor Koch's letter but Ed was a friend of his and had a great sense of humor.

"Sit here," he motioned to a chair by his desk, "and don't get mad, I am not asking you to take dictation, just write down my thoughts and help me organize them."

"Dear President Reagan, I need to bring to your attention a situation which may have escaped your view..."

Now I was paying attention. I listened and wrote, trying not to interrupt too often, for about twenty-five minutes. And during that time HF gave me some invaluable advice.

"Never accuse a President of having a bad idea. Instead, suggest that he was given bad advice from a consultant or advisor. In this case, we are informing him of the consequences of an Executive Branch action that he may or may not be aware of. A President is only as good as his top counselors and in choosing them, he is making one of his most important decisions. Always have respect for the Presidency no matter who is sitting in the Oval Office at the time; it is the core of our Republic and the public face of our government."

We proceeded to write one great letter which I was not allowed to publicize in any form even though I begged and pleaded, and I realized when we both headed home that I was fortunate that of all the 435 Members of Congress, mine was wry, private and proper and old school and the last thing he would consider was a grand-standing gesture to embarrass another public servant or bring unwarranted attention to himself. As his Press Secretary, it was a bitter pill to swallow. I had, after all, envisioned myself standing in back of the cameras or microphones while he was in make-up getting ready to grace the grand listening public with some weighty pronouncement. But now my view changed and I realized that the gift I would take away from this job was about the benefits of humility rather than hubris and the ultimate reward of being a team player.

The closed-circuit television in Will's office revealed that we were wrapping up debate on the third of thirteen amendments to a Transportation Appropriations bill.

"Why don't you go get us some sandwiches and coffee at the Members Dining room — we can eat them here while I finish this and then leave whenever this debate wraps up?" Will didn't look up from his desk while he asked me this to avoid my reaction to the obvious Girl Friday implications.

Paying for a Congressman's meal again! On the way through the Capitol, I figured out that I had probably parted with hundreds of dollars in $5 and $10 increments paying for HF's lunches or Will's midnight snacks. I felt instantly better about the letter I was about to send on both of their signatures — they owed me.

I put the food on the coffee table in front of the couch in Will's private office. The dining room in the Capitol was only selling navy bean soup, a Members Dining Room staple, and turkey sandwiches on white bread with mayonnaise, the blandest concoction I could imagine and something I would never consider eating unless I were starving.

Will sat down next to me on the couch and lifted the cover from the plate.

"What, no stuffed grape leaves, Princess Pari?" he joked. This was his new name for me ever since I had tried to feign royalty.

"Now all we need is a Red Sox game and this will be a perfect late night picnic."

He kicked off his tasseled loafers, put his stocking feet on the table and sat back to consider the closed circuit television broadcast of the House floor. The Speaker announced that a vote would be taken in twenty minutes and then the House would adjourn for the day to reconvene the next morning.

Will looked at me and eyed my kilt pin.

"Twenty minutes until the vote," he said taking my hand and kissing the upturned palm and wrist. "In that time, I plan to seduce you by attacking all of your pressure points: wrists, neck, temples," his lips touching each place as he mentioned them abandoning all thought of food.

"Are you sure you want to warn me?" I breathed already warm to his touch and no longer hungry. "I may flee this casting couch and the untoward advances of a very randy Member of Congress."

His face was buried in my neck and he pulled me under him so that we were lying prone on the standard issue furniture built and assembled in the basement work-rooms of the Capitol.

I wrapped my legs around him. "Ouch," he cursed and reached under him. With deft maneuvering practiced on many a Boston College co-ed, he undid the kilt pin with one hand, and the two halves of my skirt parted.

"Very impressive," I said bringing his face toward mine.

"I knew that pin would be your undoing," he said before kissing me, and we smiled at the pun knowing we had fifteen minutes left.

❖

Ice Cold

Adam Weiss, Director of the Immigration and Naturalization Service received two letters from the Hill by special courier. He read the first one from a friend, colleague and fellow Republican and put it on his desk. He then read the second from another member of the House Immigration Subcommittee, put it next to the previous one and picked up his phone.

"Sharon, can you tell my driver that I want to go over to the Hill? And call Hamilton Fish's office and let him know I am on my way."

I sat in HF's office, frozen to my seat, not only with extreme apprehension but because the air conditioner was broken and hovered around sixty degrees all of the time. Adam Weiss had waited patiently, oblivious to my discomfort and quite content in the refrigerated space while HF was in a Judiciary Committee hearing.

When the Congressman finally arrived, buoyant and preoccupied, he greeted Adam warmly and invited me to bring both of them up to speed on the situation. I spent a good ten minutes on the unsettled political situation in Iran with regard to the war with Iraq and another ten on why my cousin merited special consideration by the U.S. government.

Adam Weiss was not convinced. "Pari, if we make an exception for every foreign national whose life may or may not be at stake in any country facing civil or territorial war we would severely undermine the system and negate all the good work done by your boss and all the other Congressmen who crafted the immigration laws in the first place." Adam Weiss was being kind and pedantic and infuriating.

I decided to counter his argument by sitting up straighter in my chair and lowering my voice half an octave to make myself seem older.

"I understand your concerns," I told him, "however we are looking at a case with dire and immediate repercussions. This applicant will be jailed and probably tortured if returned to Iran. It's U.S. immigration policy to allow entry, especially to a minor, who will face imminent harm."

I tried to use the language of the current laws as much as possible because Adam Weiss was a lawyer's lawyer and harbored a well-known, deep respect for legal precedent.

"Allow me to interrupt with a few salient points," HF interjected, his patrician tones welcome and soothing. "From what I understand, this young man is ready to enter college. He's applying for an f-1 visa to enter the U.S. to study at a bonafide institute of higher learning in California. Isn't that right, Forood?"

"Yes, he has been accepted at San Francisco State University in California. They are expecting him for the summer term beginning July 1," I stated with more confidence than I felt.

"Right, then this is just a matter of filing the correct paperwork, Adam. An f-1 student visa should not be difficult to expedite." HF summed it up and was ready to move on to the next issue.

The esteemed Director was not swayed.

Adam Weiss reviewed the problem. "Right now, he is in France with an illegal passport, country of issuance Pakistan or I should say *black market* of Pakistan. If the French had any guts, they would have confiscated the damn thing, examined it and figured out how this network of illegals is traveling on these documents and getting around our computers," Adam said with finality.

He sat back in his chair, disgusted with government bureaucracy and dreaming of his days in private practice in Chicago.

I now realized that for him it was the bigger picture. He was not really concerned with my cousin or one individual entering this country, but the larger problem of the illegal wave of immigration from the Middle East and the black market and how to address it.

"Mr. Weiss, let me suggest something, if I may." I never called him Adam to his face.

"It seems that the applicant will have a thorough knowledge of the illegal passport business in Karachi. The French kept his passport and visa and after we examine them, we can get him here and question him about the entire operation. The least he can do is provide information on contacts and locations for the black market. Maybe with our consulate in Karachi we can put the whole picture together and really learn something useful."

I held my breath as the Director of the INS considered this plan. HF was already reading memos on different topics piled on his desk and I was slowly turning blue trying to think of an alternate argument if this one didn't work.

"Ok, I don't have a problem with that. If he agrees to be interviewed when he gets here then he will serve a useful purpose, as you put it. He will have to fly into LAX though because our San Francisco operation is too small to handle it. However, he will not get into this country with a fake Pakistani passport, Pari. I just can't bend the law whenever I feel like it. He will have to get legal travel documentation in France to accompany the f-1 visa and quite frankly, that can take up to a year."

My heart sank as I considered what Nicole and dad would have to do to make this happen.

❖

The Long Goodbye

Summer recess and members were scrambling to catch the flight back home for a flurry of constituent meetings and family gatherings. It was an election year, as all even-numbered years were, and the House adjourned early to afford the incumbents some time to 'press the flesh' in their home districts. HF was packing his brief case and we were all standing around waiting for him to leave so that we could celebrate or mourn the dog days of summer.

"Walk me down to the car, Forood, I need to talk to you," HF said. He and I rode down in the elevator discussing projects and press interviews. I thanked him once again for his personal intervention, both known and unknown, on behalf of my cousin.

He handed the taxi driver his bags and turned to me. "Pari, do you know what you're doing?"

I was flustered and surprised. For the first time, he used a personal tone — softer, more concerned — and called me by my first name. I looked at him with equal parts guilt and fear, hoping he was referring to an issue or a press release but knowing he was not.

"No, not really," I admitted. The heat was beginning to make me feel dizzy, either that or the weight of the question was simply too much to bear. "I'm being stupid, aren't I?"

"Yes," he said, "you are. And you are much too smart for that."

His face looked kind but concerned and in that instant I was simply grateful that he cared about me.

"I would expect this of a Wellesley girl, but Vassar?" He smiled, reassuring me of his support, and confirming his bias for the Seven Sisters College in his Congressional district. "Don't disappoint yourself; you know you are your harshest but ultimately fairest critic."

I hugged him not minding how inappropriate it was and he gave me a pat on the back, a gesture at once returning and confirming our duplicitous relationship of staff and friend. As I watched him drive around the Rayburn driveway onto South Capitol Street, I thought about my family and my future and the strength I would need to overcome the emotional hurdle known as Will McLean.

~

Dumbarton Oaks Gardens in Georgetown closes at 6:00 p.m. in the summer unless you happen to be a Member of Congress. I called the office using HF's name, and asked for a security guard to open the gates at dusk just as night was falling and the air was beginning to cool. Will met me at the entrance and we walked the length of the path, past the grand house given by Robert and Mildred Bliss to Harvard in 1940, and now used as a research library for the disparate subjects of Byzantine history, Garden and Landscape design, and Pre-Colombian studies.

"You want me to walk outside in a suit and tie in June in Washington?" Will had choked in disbelief when I called him with the invitation. It would be cooler at night, I countered, and deserted and ethereal. I knew he would grant me this request because he was leaving the next day and wouldn't see me for three months during the Congressional recess.

The flowers were in full bloom, bounteous and effloresced with an overabundance of petals and leaves as only flora in nature's hot-house could be. It was humid and Will took off his jacket and loosened his tie as we strolled toward the cemetery and a favorite contemplation site of Eleanor Roosevelt's where a poignant statue marks the grave of an anonymous woman who died over a century ago.

"So, you're leaving tomorrow?" I tried to sound lighthearted.

"Yes, I have constituent meetings in Boston for the next few weeks." He seemed distracted and eager to be somewhere else.

"And then some holiday time?" I couldn't help but torture myself with the query.

He looked at me and took my hand. "You know I have to act the happily married elected official. Don't punish yourself by thinking about my life at home."

And in that one word, my resolve strengthened and I was able to carry out my unenviable task. Home, he would be going home. It was not here with me, surely, and no amount of clever banter or youthful recreation would redirect his priorities or change the meaning of that word.

Home, it was a metaphor for safety and refuge. My father found it in a new country with an intriguing and wonderful family; Sahand, along with all immigrants, was seeking it through an arduous journey; and I realized that home was a calm state achieved by the cessation of internal conflict.

I stopped walking and turned to face him. I took a deep breath to steel myself to give one of the toughest confessions of my life. Even though I had rehearsed it over and over it was agony to look him in those blue eyes whose open invitation to enter and love him captured my heart.

"Will, I love you." I looked up at him; his expression did not change.

"I've never actually said it because I thought the emotion would be unwelcome in our blithe and un-complicated relationship, but I do. It may be my first real love or the only one I will ever know, but I want you to understand that you have touched me deeply and I have changed because of it."

I paused again to consider his reaction. His face was still immobile and concrete. I continued, choosing my words carefully and attempting to summon the tenacity I felt when I wasn't standing next to him. I looked at the statue guarding the grave nearby and there in a pastoral setting in Georgetown was a timeless Penelope, cast in bronze, flouting my weakness.

"When we met, I think we were drawn to each other because of a physical compatibility and there's nothing wrong with that but as I become more and more preoccupied with the state of our relationship, I realize it's demeaning and unhealthy."

I looked up at him and saw the deflating expectation my words had caused and their stubborn marks — the unfamiliar worry lines, those clear blue eyes now clouded and sandy. Never in all of our time together had I intentionally made him unhappy.

"Working on this situation with my cousin has made me realize who I am. I no longer feel apologetic for being half-Persian. I no longer hesitate when someone asks, "What kind of name is Pari Forood?" I tell them, "It's an American name and I'm a very proud citizen of this country, as is my father!" He smiled at my youthful bravado and earnestness.

"I want to be a part of the mix, Will. I want to prove that the people who came one hundred years ago and the people who come one hundred years from now can all be good for this country and what we are and what we can become."

I thought about every time the American Hostage Crisis in Iran was used as an example of a rogue nation taken over by an uncontrollable band of terrorists. The typical American now hears the word Iran or Iranian and immediately thinks enemy. I would live with this hard, implacable label and work to soften it or alter the perception, one person at a time.

"I need to stop being obsessed with you and when I will see you and how we will meet. I think I was partially in love with the clandestine nature of it all. Secrets in Washington seem so appropriate, but I can't do it anymore."

I shook my head slowly back and forth thinking of the times I sat waiting for his call or his knock and never hearing them; of living on the memory of a smile as I passed him in the hallway or a quick kiss in the Rayburn garage. I had set my sights on this star in the heavens and no amount of gravitational pull would convince me that I couldn't one day drag him to me, until now.

And then I began to cry.

"I'm better for knowing you, Will. Every part of me, the Persian part and the American part, blossomed under your gaze and care." I smiled slightly through my tears and we shared a silent memory of the times he told me I was breathtaking and more interesting than anyone he had ever met.

"I will forever be grateful for all you have given me but I can't love someone who can't openly love me back." I choked out the last few words and looked away, trying to hide my emotional vulnerability.

He exhaled a huge lungful of air, making me think he had been holding his breath the whole time. He looked at me long and hard, resigned and possibly relieved that the moment he knew was coming had arrived. His gaze was not critical or hurt but assessing, measuring the weight of my words and determining the effort it would take to accept or refute them.

His arms rose and he drew me deep into the folds of his suit and his smell and the small, privileged circle of his affection. We stood hugging for a long time before he kissed me and said with emotion and regret, "In my heart, I will always love you too." And then he turned and left.

❖

Paris Solution

Sahand, Nicole, Marie Claude and Bob were all sitting in the Chevron offices on Avenue de France contemplating the latest dictum from the American Embassy: "No passport, no visa."

"His Pakistani passport has been confiscated." Marie Claude said. "And it is out of the question to apply for a French passport when you are not a French citizen."

Nicole looked despondent. "Maybe Pari can have her Congressman speak to the Immigration people in the U.S. and they can waive the passport requirement."

Bob Forood stood up to pace. "I already spoke to her. She said that the Director of the American Immigration Service was adamant. Sahand has to travel with some form of identification, something official with a photograph that identifies him and attests to his nationality and birth date so they can check it against lists of international criminals. She says that we will just have to figure out a way to get him documented here even if it takes a long time."

"But he is here on a tourist visa," Marie Claude reminded them. "He has three months before they start checking on him. Besides, I promised the Head of the

Border Police at Charles de Gaulle that he would only be here a few days until his travel to America could be arranged."

Sahand sat in a chair too stunned and depleted to speak.

He would have to go back. They would come and arrest him, put him on a plane and send him back to Iran. He sat without hope thinking only of his parents and their crushed spirits at hearing the news. This morning when they called Tehran, his uncle tried to sound optimistic to his parents, especially considering Pari's high level meeting with the Director of the U.S. Immigration Service, but his father had recognized defeat and ended the call wishing them luck with a voice absent of expectation. Sahand knew that his father had to console his mother who was probably prostrate with fear and one of her migraine headaches. Since the Revolution she could not get the medication she needed and suffered through paralyzing pain in her dark bedroom with only a cold compress for relief.

Marie Claude stood to leave when Nicole stopped her with a distracted wave.

"Wait a minute, I just thought of something." Nicole was both excited and agitated, standing to engage her friend and question her directly.

"Marie, remember last year when you helped your Turkish maid get her brother into this country?"

"Yes," Marie said, "but he had a Turkish passport and I just helped him get a work permit so that he could get a job."

Nicole continued to speak, impatient to express her ideas. "But didn't you tell me that your maid would be his official sponsor and she needed French documentation to do so? You were complaining and whining that her Turkish passport and French work permit weren't enough for the French officials. You said we were a country of ridiculous rules and regulations and too much paperwork. Do you remember?" Nicole moved closer to her friend, willing her to understand her train of thought. All eyes were on her.

"Yes, yes I remember but I fail to see how this affects our current situation," Marie Claude said.

"You were able to obtain a *carte d'identité* for her, I remember you telling me that some people use it instead of a passport, that some countries accept it as sufficient travel documentation!" Nicole continued, hardly able to contain her enthusiasm.

"Mon Dieu, you are right! She just needed a French address and some help from my office and we were able to issue a *carte d'identité* in about a week."

The atmosphere in the room shifted from dejection to anxious euphoria within minutes. The gloom was now coated with a benign glaze of hope and possibility. Sahand looked to his uncle to see if he was as optimistic as the two excited women and Bob's expression echoed the brightened atmosphere.

"I will find out from Pari if an official French Identification Card is enough to accompany the f-1 visa," Bob said. He picked up the phone and all eyes were on him as wires and satellites and cables made the world seem like a small, connected space of individuals coming together to accomplish the impossible.

❖

Staff Run the World

I picked up the phone in my office, pushed one of the Watts long distance lines and dialed the INS office at LAX airport. With Sahand's imminent departure from France and his freshly minted *carte d'identité* and student f-1 visa signed by the Ambassador himself, I couldn't foresee any stumbling blocks. I had no idea who would interview my cousin upon his arrival in this country but I was determined to speak with them first and make sure they knew they would be dealing with a scared and exhausted teenager and not a hardened criminal. With my Northern California bias, I didn't trust anyone from Los Angeles to do anything but overact and I would use Adam Weiss' influence if needed.

"Bud Greeley," answered the agent. I tried to determine what type of person he was from the intonation. At three thousand miles away, it was impossible to know if my contact had a bad day much less a disappointing life and I decided to be as personable as possible. I was determined to sound as if I were asking a favor as opposed to imposing the will of Congress on a small representative of the Executive Branch on the "Left Coast" who probably wished he were at the beach instead of catching smugglers.

"Bud, this is Pari Forood in Washington D.C. I'm with Congressman Hamilton Fish of New York." I paused, hoping this agent knew our relationship to the INS and its purse strings and policy manifestos. If he did, he was either too impressed to respond or too angry at any intrusion from Congress for his a) salary b) pension, or c) uncompensated overtime, and was therefore rendered mute.

I continued in my friendliest and most sympathetic tone.

"I can imagine the amount of calls you must get from elected officials asking for special treatment or consideration and I just wanted to give you a heads-up about a letter or call coming from Adam Weiss' office about a young man traveling on an official French Identification Card and f-1 visa with expedited approval stamps. He's arriving from Paris this week — Wednesday in fact, on Air France flight #18 and his English, while certainly competent, is not as good as his Farsi!"

I laughed and tried to detect a reaction from across the phone lines. Still hearing no utterance from my adversary, I proceeded to fill in those uncomfortable silences that had always turned me into a blathering fool in certain social situations.

"Bud, I notice you're not saying much and I just want you to know that I appreciate your position in this matter. We're not asking you to compromise your integrity or anything, it's just that the person arriving on Wednesday is a political refugee who has come a long way under stressful circumstances. Adam Weiss has approved his entry; however, he wants his agents, in other words *you*, to question our constituent about how he obtained a counterfeit passport in Pakistan even though it was confiscated by the French two weeks ago."

Now I felt I had said enough and I waited patiently for Bud Greeley of the INS to speak.

208

"What did you say his name is?" Bud's voice seemed non-committal. I repeated it for him spelling my last name just as I do every time I make a reservation or leave a phone message.

"Have you received a communication from the Director's office about him?" I asked.

"Not yet," Bud said, "but paper moves slowly down the line here. Is his name the same as yours or did I hear you wrong when you introduced yourself?"

"You heard me correctly," I told him. "He's actually my cousin, not a constituent of ours, but Congressman Fish as well as Congressman McLean of Massachusetts are helping to expedite his entry into the U.S."

Bud was writing everything down on his standard issue, U.S. government approved office equipment pad, cradling the phone on his shoulder, and trying to talk at the same time.

"That's nice of them. I can think of about a million people who could use that kind of special treatment."

And now my heart sank. I detected sarcasm and bitter stains on his words. Whatever this man had been through during his tenure at the INS, he was marked by it and soured. He could not stop Sahand from entering the country once the Director of the INS had already approved it but he could be difficult in the interview or detain him for hours just to prove a point.

"Listen Bud, I don't know anything about you and you certainly don't know anything about me, but I am first generation on my father's side. He came to this country to go to school and learn about America first hand so that he could spread the knowledge and promise so inherent in our system and way of life to another part of the world. As it

209

turned out, he met my mother and stayed here, but all of his family is subject to the human rights atrocities happening daily in the Islamic Republic of Iran. My cousin was drafted into an army of children who are told that the greatest glory is to die in a border war with Iraq. This is where we call upon the better angels of our nature as Abraham Lincoln once said, and allow this person to possibly thrive in an environment free from the xenophobe currently running his country!" And now I was on a roll.

"Many people from truck drivers in Iran to high ranking officials in the French government have gone out of their way to help this kid. We've strung together a network stretching halfway across the world to give him access to the things he needed to get out of Iran and into the U.S. When I say he would face harm if returned, I am referring to sure and certain death."

I did not regret using hyperbole to make my case. I felt I had to pierce the thick skin of this bureaucrat's mundane routine and find the inner core of his humanity. Each person I had met or engaged in this mission had reached inside themselves to a place hidden and guarded by their commonplace life. I was determined to convince this last custodian of America's borders that the latest pilgrims are just as essential as the first.

Bud Greeley stared into the notes he had been taking during the long soliloquy and thought of the man outside the mosque. *We took nothing with us but the clothes on our backs.* He thought of every immigrant he had sent back to Guatemala, Africa, and the Philippines, who had begged and pleaded to stay. He inhaled the problem and exhaled the tight singular solution through lips taut and dry with conviction.

We took nothing with us but the shirts on our backs, he said under his breath, but I heard it faintly and smiled. Three thousand miles away, I understood a man faced with an impossible mission, willing to help, and I recognized a kindred spirit had been added to the motley group of heroes and characters who were quite possibly responsible for the salvation of a life.

Bud listened while I recounted Sahand's journey from Tehran to Karachi to Paris and, if all went well, Los Angeles and then ultimately San Francisco. He asked questions and took notes so that he could interview Sahand and file a report that would appease and impress his boss, Adam Weiss, and his strong desire for answers. He felt important for the first time in his job and thought of the act of helping one person and how many lives would be touched in the ripple of cause and effect. *It's our chance,* he thought, *for all of those divergent actors on a grand and global stage marked by religious, socio-economic, cultural, and ethnic differences to pool their talents and create a success story. I am only glad to be a small part of it.*

"Bud, you're the best," I told him. "I realize you have to work with us because of the Director's letter but I can tell you won't give my cousin a hard time when you question him. Your cooperation is essential to the ultimate success of this operation and I really appreciate it."

"By the way," Bud added before we hung up, "I just remembered where I've heard your name before. It's such a distinct name I always wondered about the ethnic derivation. Wasn't there another Forood who was some kind of tennis star at Stanford University a few years ago?"

"Yes, Lele, my sister. She's a touring pro now." This was a source of great pride in my family and I never tried to disguise the pleasure in my voice.

"And don't I recall that she's from San Francisco?" Bud sounded absolutely hopeful and I couldn't imagine why he should remember this obscure fact.

"We were born in the city but my family moved out to Mill Valley in Marin County when we were very young," I told him.

I loved to talk about family history and I wondered how I could elaborate without boring him. Before I had the chance, Bud's muffled cheer reached across the phone lines to me and I spent the next thirty minutes hearing about his wedding, kids, dogs and dislike of L.A. We talked about the Bay Area and the best place to buy ice cream (Bud's), hamburgers (In and Out) and tea (Peet's). He told me of his frustrations with his job and the need for leadership and guidance from Washington on the issue of immigration. I assured him we were doing the best we could but that the problem would only get worse as the east poured west for education, jobs, opportunity and freedom.

I knew I had an ally and I thought of providence or fate or sheer dumb luck that led us to this agent of change and redemption and all of the people Sahand had come into contact with along his journey and their mutual kindred spirit and elevated sense of purpose. Actually, we were fortunate that greed in some cases and family responsibility and friendship in others stacked our deck and dealt us a winning hand.

I will never underestimate the kismet, to use a word of Arabic etymology, present or visited upon all of us who were part of this magic carpet ride across three continents and countless bureaucracies and government officials, not to mention shady characters of questionable repute.

I thanked Bud profusely again and again for his help and hung up with his assurance that he would call if there was a problem. He promised to escort Sahand to his connecting flight to San Francisco and buy him a classic American hot dog in the airport on the way. I did not spoil the intrinsic kindness in that gesture by telling him it would not be his first one.

Bud became energized with his role in this case. He felt vindicated for every potential citizen he had returned to his country of origin with good reason or not. He knew that no matter how many Ambassadors or Congressmen or Directors in Washington were monitoring the movement of this young man, it was his responsibility to assure the safe journey of one embattled and weary individual home to his ultimate destination.

❖

Lucky Me

Interminable Washington rubber chicken dinners — I had been to more of them than there are steps on the Lincoln Memorial — but, I owed HF and decided that I would honor his request to represent him at any dinner, lunch or Arbor Day ceremony in gratitude for his help. My cousin was en route to California and I had made an ally at the INS Field Office at Los Angeles International Airport. My uncle was weak with relief and my aunt had stopped crying and thanking us. I felt a deep well of accomplishment fill from two spouts of competency and loyalty.

My table at this particular function was packed with "suits" from the Hill and its environs all representing someone slightly more important, including me. I took note of an attractive man, in a bow tie and old-fashioned tortoise shell glasses, who seemed uncomfortable and I decided that he must be new. With proclamations and speeches on the horizon, I took pity on him and decided to fill him in.

"Don't worry, it will all be over soon and you will be able to go home," I consoled him.

He seemed startled by my attention and after faltering over his words, finally introduced himself as a doctoral candidate from Princeton who was temporarily advising the

House Foreign Affairs Committee. I told him my name and shook his hand. He held it for a long moment and looked deeply into my face.

"You have an ancient name; 'Pari' means fairy, doesn't it? And wasn't Forood a warrior from the *Shahnameh*?"

I was stunned and couldn't help but smile. "I'm amazed with your knowledge of obscure ancient Middle Eastern references."

He smiled sheepishly. "It's both my field and my passion," he explained. "I have a contract to start teaching at Princeton next semester. I'm just here lending some expertise to the Middle East section of the committee staff."

I nodded, instantly understanding the type of course he would be offering to the undergraduate population of the Ivy League.

"I'm assuming that your class will be mostly about ancient Greece and Rome and the slaughtering of the Persians and the justification of our current policy of advanced disengagement and hostility," I said rhetorically.

His eyes widened in protest. "On the contrary, the course I've outlined will highlight all of the advances introduced by the ancient Middle Eastern cultures as well as a cursory reading of the Shahnameh and Persian art, architecture and history."

My face softened at my mistake. The world wasn't producing Iran-haters after all.

"I wish I could take it," I told him, repentant and visibly impressed.

His eyebrows shot up over his round tortoise shell glasses. "Considering your background, you could probably teach it."

I put my hand over his and squeezed slightly. "That's nice of you to say, but I'm just an ignorant American with much to learn about her heritage. All I really know is that for some instinctual reason, I'm proud of who I am and my incongruent parts and my history and my relatives. As American as I feel and as much as I love this country, I will always know that I come from a place and a people that started the world."

"Lucky you," he said, "I'm just third generation Irish-Italian."

I looked at him and my eyes misted slightly as I thought back on every time I said my name was Lebanese or Egyptian or lied about my father's accent or my grand-mother's religion. I looked down and considered my hands and arms with their olive skin that tans and never burns, my desire to respect or at least listen to every accent trying so hard to form foreign English words, and my reverence for America and its shining possibilities reflected in each new face. And at that moment I finally felt a certain sense of peace.

Yes, I thought, *lucky me.*

My father and me, 2002

Epilogue

There were times in this process when I was convinced we would never be successful. When my cousin was en route to Pakistan, he was out of communication and his parents were convinced he had been robbed and killed. In Pakistan where the black market was the only vehicle for most necessities, it was a miracle that a seventeen year old was able to locate and work with outlaws to buy a passport that passed Pakistani official inspection and enter France with mild repercussions. And in an impatient and stressed American embassy inundated with visa applications from third world refugees, we feared that even with our connections and an official French Identity Card, my cousin's plight would be ignored. The fact that we overcame all of these obstacles makes me think that we were not acting alone in guiding this immigrant toward freedom and a new home.

When my father arrived in 1947, the U.S. was welcoming students with open arms. In my childhood being half-Persian was a curiosity and a distinction. The world had changed and in 1984, we were witnessing the underpinnings of unrest in the Middle East that would dominate our foreign policy for the foreseeable future and declare a new and formidable enemy. Middle Eastern countries like Iran were not relying on their colorful past or traditions to augment modernization, they were conjuring ancient tomes to justify the rejection of any innovations or ideas which would confirm the superiority of the Imperialists. Oil gave them power, religion gave them a reason, and disparity in a world ruled by the West gave them a purpose. The glory of Ancient Persia was lost to the present reality of fanaticism and violence.

After that conversation about taking Farsi in college, my daughter went on to the Elliot School of International Affairs at George Washington University and specialized in 'conflict resolution' in the Middle East. (The family joke is that she will never be out of a job.) She is part Persian, part WASP, part Jewish and as idealistic about America in 2014 as her grandfather was when he landed in New York sixty-seven years ago. The speech I wrote in my idealistic youth on Capitol Hill for a Naturalization ceremony still resonates today, "We are all immigrants in this country, judged not by our ancestry but by our accomplishments."

So what is the answer, the magic formula to move this nation of newcomers and descendants of newcomers toward a more peaceful coexistence in a world marred with hostility and aggression? There is a glimmer of hope: as I write this, Iranian and U.S. officials are at the negotiating table in Geneva. For the first time in thirty-five years, the Presidents of both countries spoke to each other on the phone and President Rouhani of Iran has a Twitter account.

But what is our role, what can we do to lessen tensions in the world and foster peace? Can we be that oasis of geniality where assimilation is encouraged and promoted on a backdrop of tolerance?

We can try.

We can remind our children and grandchildren of their rich traditions while supporting their successes in their new and native country. We can encourage them to honor their adopted home while studying the customs of their ancestors to find the ancient connection that will illuminate who they are. We can teach and embrace the origins of our freedoms and the nation that was founded upon them. We can remind ourselves that each new and different face means strength in diversity and innovation. And perhaps if we adopt a national policy of developing the talents of our immigrants and their children, we will finally have a shot at winning the World Cup!

As I regard the future, I see the succession of subliminal forces as powerful and regular as the tide flowing un-impeded in the veins of my children. The continuity of values and traits as they are handed down from generation to generation becomes our legacy. It's neither good nor bad. It's not a value judgment or a litmus test for appropriate behavior. We are who we are and all the tea in the world won't change that fact. What a comforting thought.

I involuntarily mimic my father's habits more and more. I think about the past, what has shaped me, what will influence my daughters, how much their Persian ancestry will affect their lives and routines. They seem so American to me, as I must have seemed to my father, as all American-born children of immigrants must seem to their parents. And yet in the depth of a dark brown eye or the love of an exotic spice I warm to behold the mark of my ancestors on this new generation.

I pray for an immense tolerance and fortitude in a world divided by the excuse and excess of sectarian differences. I will to them the patience it will take to know and under-stand how to help unify this disparate world of feuding cultures and the knowledge to quell this giant beast threatening to ruin the shining accomplishments of civiliza-tions in their prime.

If anyone is up to the task, it will be them, the daughters of a first generation American, with a Persian grandfather and an American grandmother and the diverse history of pioneers and princes, statesmen and soldiers.

Thirty years ago, my cousin arrived in Los Angeles, talked for three hours with INS officials, ate a hot dog with them and flew to San Francisco. He now has a family and a home. His children are first generation Americans, like me, with a Persian name and father.

There is no more fun-loving and amiable nationality than the Persians, no people who like to laugh or dance or get together for the pure joy of shared conviviality than they. If ever you have the chance to attend a party or share a meal or a conversation, jump at the opportunity, you will never regret it.

❖

Excerpts from "Paradise and the Peri" from *Lalla Rookh*
(1817) by Sir Thomas More (1779-1852)

One morn a Peri at the gate
of Eden stood disconsolate;
And as she listened to the Springs
of Life within like music flowing
And caught the light upon her wings
Thro' the half-open portal glowing,
She wept to think her recreant race
Should e'er have lost that glorious place!

A fairy prostrate with grief, weeps at the gates of heaven.
Her tears fall in streams from her magical face and soak the
ground before her. She has been expelled from paradise
and denied re-entry by the powerful angel who holds the
fate of all in his celestial grasp. As she lays weeping, a
strange light descends near her and as it grows brighter it
takes the shape of a great being with gold tipped wings.

"Why do you cry?" the angel asks the fairy.

"It is my punishment — I am not allowed into your
heavenly home. I am disconsolate at my fate," she con-
fesses. The angel takes pity on the Peri.

"Nymph of a fair but erring line!"
Gently he said, "One hope is thine.
'Tis written in the Book of Fate,
The Peri yet may be forgiven
Who brings to this Eternal gate

222

The Gift that is most dear to Heaven!
Go seek it and redeem thy sin —
'Tis sweet to let the Pardoned in."

The angel tells the fairy that if she brings to heaven the gift most cherished by God, she will be pardoned and allowed to enter. Upon hearing these words, the Peri flies everywhere looking for the gift to offer the Almighty. As she wanders from far off land to far off land she spies a battle-field at the end of a war with many brave soldiers dead and dying. The despot Mahmoud claims victory and with his triumphant bravado, offers charity to a young warrior who was his enemy. The young soldier, true to his dying breath, flings an arrow at the tyrant as one last attempt to secure freedom for his people.

False flew the shaft tho' pointed well;
The Tyrant lived, the Hero fell! —
Yet marked the Peri where he lay,
And when the rush of war was past
Swiftly descending on a ray
Of morning light she caught the last —
Last glorious drop his heart had shed
Before its free-born spirit fled!

The arrow misses its mark and the Hero falls to the ground, dead. The Peri takes to Heaven's Gate the last drop of the patriot's blood as her offering, but the gates do not open to her. "This is not the gift dearest to God," the angel tells her.

She then flies to Egypt, where the plague is raging, and sees a young man dying. Crippled by his disease, disfigured by sores, the young man gazes at an imminent death. His lover, pristine with beauty and love, looks on him with adoration, blind to his present plight. While others pull at her to quit the contagion where she will surely be infected and die, she smiles, takes the hand of her betrothed, lays down beside him, and as the sores begin to multiply on her skin, the smile never leaves her face.

> *"Sleep," said the Peri, as softly she stole*
> *The farewell sigh of that vanishing soul,*
> *As true as e'er warmed a woman's breast —*
> *"Sleep on, in visions of odor rest*
> *In balmier airs than ever yet stirred*
> *The enchanted pile of that lonely bird*
> *Who sings at the last his own death-lay*
> *And in music and perfume dies away!"*
> *Thus saying, from her lips she spread*
> *Unearthly breathings thro' the place*
> *And shook her sparkling wreath and shed*
> *Such lustre o'er each paly face*
> *That like two lovely saints they seemed,*
> *Upon the eve of doomsday taken*
> *From their dim graves in order sleeping;*
> *While that benevolent Peri beamed*
> *Like their good angel calmly keeping*
> *Watch o'er them til their souls would waken.*

The Peri witnesses the ultimate sacrifice of love and takes to Heaven's Gate the last sigh of that selfless damsel; but the offering is not good enough to open the gates to her. "This is not the gift dearest to God," the angel tells her.

"But, ah! Even Peri's hopes are vain —
Again the Fates forbade, again
The immortal barrier closed — "Not yet,"
The Angel said with regret.
He shut from her that glimpse of glory —
"True was the maiden and her story
Written in light o'er Alla's head
By seraph eyes shall long be read.
But, Peri, see — the crystal bar
of Eden moves not — holier far
Than even this sigh the boon must be
That opens the Gates of Heaven for thee."

Lastly, the Peri flies for many days and nights and finally she spots an innocent child playing in a field. His aura is white as snow and his cares as light as clouds. Near the child, in a grove of trees, the fairy sees a man dismount from his horse. His evil history, written like the frieze on the outside of an urn, boasts unspeakable crimes and sins, blackening his soul for eternity.

And yet he gazes on the boy and is transfixed.

Yet tranquil now that man of crime
(As if the balmy evening time
Softened his spirit) looked and lay,
Watching the rosy infants play: —
Tho' still whene'er his eye by chance
Fell on the boys, its lucid glance
Met that unclouded, joyous gaze
As torches that have burnt all night
Tho' some impure and godless rite,
Encounter morning's glorious rays.

At that moment, the vesper call sounds, and the child kneels down to prayer. The aged sinner watches in wonder as the child forces him to remember a more innocent time in his life.

"There was a time," he said, in mild
Heart-humbled tones — "thou blessed child!
When young and haply pure as thou
I looked and prayed like thee — but now" —
He hung his head — each nobler aim
And hope and feeling which had slept
From boyhood's hour that instant came
Fresh o'er him and he wept — he wept!

The old man weeps with repentance, and kneels to pray beside the child. The Peri watches as the sinner, gazing on innocence and purity, repents his sins and prays with the child.

"Oh, is it not thus, thou man of sin,
The precious tears of repentance fall?
Tho' foul thy fiery plagues within
One heavenly drop hath dispelled them all!"
And now — behold him kneeling there
By the child's side, in humble prayer,
While the same sunbeam shines upon
The guilty and the guiltless one.
And hymns of joy proclaim thro' Heaven
The triumph of a Soul Forgiven!

As the sunset and heaven beckon, the Peri watches the two figures hunched in mutual humiliation before God. The old man weeps openly shedding his sins and asking forgiveness. In speechless response, a celestial light falls upon his tears and the Peri knows her task is almost done.

> *'Twas when the golden orb had set,*
> *While on their knees they lingered yet,*
> *There fell a light more lovely far*
> *Than ever came from sun or star,*
> *Upon the tear that, warm and meek,*
> *Dewed that repentant sinner's cheek.*
> *To mortal eye this light might seem*
> *A northern flash or meteor beam —*
> *But well the enraptured Peri knew*
> *'Twas a bright smile the Angel threw*
> *From heaven's gate to hail that tear*
> *Her harbinger of glory near!*

The Peri flies back to the Gates of Heaven to present the angel with the tear of a repentant sinner. And she rejoices.

> *"Farewell, ye vanishing flowers that shone*
> *In my fairy wreath so bright an' brief; —*
> *Oh! what are the brightest that e'er have blown*
> *To the lote-tree springing by Alla's throne*
> *Whose flowers have a soul in every leaf.*
> *Joy, joy forever, — my task is done —*
> *The Gates are past and Heaven is won!"*

And the Gates of Light fly open to receive her gift.

❖

❖

Acknowledgements

As I told my daughter in the short video available on my publisher's website, writing this book was cathartic on so many levels. I had been writing it for such a long time and reminiscing, remembering, postulating about the implications for national immigration policy; to view the finished product is nothing short of miraculous.

Thank you to Amy Johnson and Libby Mitchell of West Cornwall Publishing. The first time I uttered the words, 'my publishers' a chill went through me and I felt like the luckiest person on Earth. Thank you to my family for lending me their stories and histories, all of which make me whole. And thank you to my daughters who are the inspiration for everything I do.

Professionally I need to acknowledge Madeleine Albright whose memoir was enlightening and encouraging, the Congressional Management Foundation which provided me with hours of entertaining reading, and Harvard sociologist Horace Kallen whom I quote in my Introduction. I've read and enjoyed *All the Shah's Men* by Steven Kinzer many times and treasure the copy given to me by my father.

❖